Coffee Break Python - Mastery Workout

99 Tricky Python Puzzles to Push You to Programming Mastery

Lukas Rieger, Adrian Chan, and Christian Mayer

May 24, 2020

A puzzle a day to learn, code, and play.

Dedication

This book is dedicated to the vivid Finxter community of ambitious Python coders.

Table of Contents

Table of Contents		iv
1	Introduction	1
2	Elo 1300-1400	12
3	Elo 1400-1500	16
4	Elo 1500-1600	21
5	Elo 1600-1700	30
6	Elo 1700-1800	39
7	Elo 1800-1900	56
8	Elo 1900-2000	81

9   Elo 2000-2100   120

10 Elo 2100-2200   136

11 Elo 2200-2300   142

12 Elo 2300-*   148

13 Final Remarks   153

14 Python Cheat Sheets   166

Long Table of Contents

Table of Contents   iv

1 Introduction   **1**
   1.1 Why Code Puzzles?   3
   1.2 Elo   5
   1.3 How to Use This Book   7
   1.4 Test & Train   7

2 Elo 1300-1400   **12**
   2.1 Basic For Loop   13
   2.2 Variable Scope III   14

3 Elo 1400-1500   **16**
   3.1 Boolean Conversion   17
   3.2 Tuple Constructor   18
   3.3 Popping List Elements   19

4 Elo 1500-1600 **21**

    4.1 Extending Lists 22

    4.2 list.extend() vs. list.append() 23

    4.3 List Objects 24

    4.4 Python Basic Set Operations 25

    4.5 Length Arithmetik 26

    4.6 Print Arguments 27

    4.7 Dictionary Keys 28

5 Elo 1600-1700 **30**

    5.1 String Find 31

    5.2 Slicing 32

    5.3 List Arithmetic I 33

    5.4 List Arithmetic II 34

    5.5 Variable Scope II 35

    5.6 String Find 36

    5.7 Zip Heterogeneous Lists 37

6 Elo 1700-1800 **39**

    6.1 Boolean Integer Relationship 40

    6.2 Slice Assignment Basics 41

    6.3 List Multiplication 42

    6.4 Integers in Memory 43

    6.5 Slice Assignment 44

    6.6 Maximum With Key 45

    6.7 Maximum With Key 46

    6.8 Variable Scoping Lists 47

    6.9 Dictionary Comprehension 48

6.10 Minimum with Key 49

6.11 Slice Assignment 50

6.12 Keyword Arguments 51

6.13 Assignment Confusion 52

6.14 Slice Assignment 53

6.15 Unpacking Strings 54

7   Elo 1800-1900   **56**

7.1   While ... Else Loop 57

7.2   Enumerating Dictionaries 58

7.3   Negative Slice Indices 59

7.4   Iterable Unpacking 60

7.5   Default Arguments in Constructor 61

7.6   List Arithmetic III 62

7.7   Default Function Arguments 63

7.8   Class Variables and Inheritance 64

7.9   Integer and String Conversions 66

7.10 Finding Substrings 67

7.11 Integer and Float Conversions 68

7.12 List Operations 69

7.13 Variable Scope I 70

7.14 Arbitrary Arguments 71

7.15 Dictionary Unpacking and Assignment . 72

7.16 List Object 73

7.17 Recursion 74

7.18 Ternary Operator 76

7.19 Memory Allocation 77

7.20 Scope of Instance Attributes 78

8 Elo 1900-2000   **81**
  8.1 Dictionary Conditional Insert 82
  8.2 Dictionary Initialization 83
  8.3 List Comprehension Arithmetic 84
  8.4 Overriding 86
  8.5 Understanding Iterables I 88
  8.6 Overriding 2.0 89
  8.7 List Arithmetic (Multiplication) 91
  8.8 Unpacking for Pros 92
  8.9 Customizing the Minimum 93
  8.10 Default Arguments 94
  8.11 Unpacking Reloaded 95
  8.12 Class Variables Reloaded 96
  8.13 Swapping Values in Instance Methods . . 97
  8.14 Slicing Confusion 99
  8.15 Short Circuiting 100
  8.16 Dictionary Comprehension 101
  8.17 Dictionary Pop 103
  8.18 Class Variable vs Instance Attributes . . 104
  8.19 Dictionary Unpacking 106
  8.20 Instance and Attribute 108
  8.21 Parallel Assignment 109
  8.22 Understanding Iterables II 110
  8.23 Advanced Mapping 112
  8.24 Tuple Concatenation 113
  8.25 Class vs Instance Variables 114
  8.26 Default Object Arguments 116

8.27 Default Function Arguments and Scoping 118

9 Elo 2000-2100   **120**
  9.1   String Representation 121
  9.2   List Operations 122
  9.3   Slicing Tuples 123
  9.4   Zip 124
  9.5   Zip Iteration 125
  9.6   Being Precise 127
  9.7   Set Default Dicts 128
  9.8   Sequence Comparison 130
  9.9   Definition of Instance Variables 131
  9.10 Name Resolution in Classes 133

10 Elo 2100-2200   **136**
  10.1 Overriding 3.0 137
  10.2 Short Circuiting 139
  10.3 Boolean Operator Precedence 140

11 Elo 2200-2300   **142**
  11.1 Operator Precedence 143
  11.2 Custom Sum 145
  11.3 Global and Local Variable Scopes 146

12 Elo 2300-*   **148**
  12.1 Mutability of Objects 149
  12.2 The Complement Operator 151

13 Final Remarks **153**

Where to Go From Here? 154

14 Python Cheat Sheets **166**

14.1 Keywords 166

14.2 Basic Data Types 170

14.3 Complex Data Types 173

14.4 Classes 178

14.5 Functions and Tricks 181

— 1 —

Introduction

The main driver for mastery is neither a character trait nor talent. Mastery comes from intense, structured training. Mark Zuckerberg, the founder of Facebook, reached mastery at a young age as a result of coding for more than 10,000 hours—laying the foundation to a billion-user company at the age of 20. He was committed and passionate about coding and worked long nights to develop his skills. He was anything but an overnight success.

Here's what we, the authors, know about you: you're an aspiring coder, and you seek ways to improve your coding skills. How do we know? Simple statistics: only a small fraction of people reads books in their fields. You don't spend money and time on a book if you don't seek to advance your skills.

Advancing your coding skills is, ultimately, one of the most powerful things you can do to advance the efficiency of society overall and, thus, your financial and social reward from society. Machines work diligently 24 hours per day, seven days per week. If you're a good programmer, your programs will provide a never-ending stream of value to you, your family, your state, your country, and your fellow men. Why? Because machines replicate and automate your ability to create value. Learning to code will give you a powerful tool to make you a respectable member of society and to provide you with confidence and financial freedom.

The *Coffee Break Python - Mastery Workout* is the second workbook and the fifth book of the *Coffee Break Python* series of Python textbooks. In a way, it's an extension of its predecessor *Coffee Break Python Workbook*[1]—but with 99 brand-new code puzzles teaching new Python concepts, it stands on its own.

This book aims to be a stepping stone on your path to becoming a Python master. It contains 15-25 hours of Python training using one of the most efficient learning techniques: *practice testing*. This technique is guaranteed to improve your ability to read, write, and understand Python source code.

The idea is that you solve code puzzles. A *code puzzle*

---

[1] https://blog.finxter.com/coffee-break-python-workbook/

is an educational snippet of source code that teaches a single computer science concept by activating your curiosity and involving you in the learning process. The code puzzles in this book have an intermediate to advanced difficulty level.

How does it work? In essence, you play the Python interpreter and compute the output of each code snippet in your head. Then you check whether you were right. Using the accompanying feedback and explanations, you will adapt and improve your coding skills over time.

To make this idea a reality, we developed the online coding academy `Finxter.com`. The next section explains the advantages of the Finxter method of puzzle-based learning. If you already know about the benefits of puzzle-based learning from previous books and want to dive right into the puzzles, you can skip the following section and start at Chapter 2.

1.1 Why Code Puzzles?

Robust scientific evidence shows that active learning doubles students' learning performance. In a study on this matter, test scores of active learners improved by more than a grade compared to their passive learning counterparts.[2] Not using active learning techniques wastes your time and hinders you if you want to reach your full potential. Switching to active learning is a simple tweak that instantly improves your performance.

Active learning requires the student to interact with the material, rather than simply consume it. It is student-centric rather than teacher-centric. Great active learning techniques are asking and answering questions, self-testing, teaching, and summarizing.

A popular study shows that one of the best learning techniques is *practice testing.*[3] In this technique, you test your knowledge before you have learned everything. Rather than *learning by doing*, it's *learning by testing*.

The study argues that students must feel safe during these tests. Therefore, the tests must be low-stakes, i.e., students have little to lose. After the test, students get feedback on how well they did. The study shows that practice testing boosts long-term retention. Solving a daily code puzzle is not just another learning technique—it is one of the best.

Although active learning is twice as effective, most books focus on passive learning. The author delivers informa-

---

[2]https://en.wikipedia.org/wiki/Active_learning#Research_evidence

[3]http://journals.sagepub.com/doi/abs/10.1177/1529100612453266

tion; the student passively consumes it. Some programming books include active learning elements by adding tests or by asking the reader to try out the code examples. Yet, we've always found this impractical when reading on the train, bus or in bed. If these active elements drop out, learning becomes 100% passive again.

Fixing this mismatch between research and everyday practice drove me to write this book series about puzzle-based learning. In contrast to other books, this book makes active learning a first-class citizen. Solving code puzzles is an inherent active learning technique. You must figure out the solution yourself for every single puzzle. Before you study the correct solution, your knowledge gap is already wide open. Thus, you are mentally prepared to digest new material.

1.2 The Elo Rating for Python

Pick any sport you've always loved to play. How good are you compared to others? The Elo rating—initially developed to rate the skills of chess players—answers this question with surprising accuracy. The higher the Elo rating, the better the chess player. Now, we simply take this concept and use it to rate your Python skills.

Table 1.1 shows the ranks for each Elo rating level. The table is an opportunity for you to estimate your Python

Elo rating	Rank
2500	World Class
2400-2500	Grandmaster
2300-2400	International Master
2200-2300	Master
2100-2200	National Master
2000-2100	Master Candidate
1900-2000	Authority
1800-1900	Expert
1700-1800	Professional
1600-1700	Experienced Intermediate
1500-1600	Intermediate
1400-1500	Experienced Learner
1300-1400	Learner
1200-1300	Scholar
1100-1200	Autodidact
1000-1100	Beginner
0-1000	Basic Knowledge

Table 1.1: Elo ratings and skill levels.

skill level. In the following, we'll describe how you can use this book to test your Python skills.

1.3 How to Use This Book

This book contains 99 (tricky) code puzzles and explanations to test and train your Python skills. The Elo ranges from 1500 to 2300 points (between *intermediate* and *Master* level in the table). This book is perfect for you if you are beyond intermediate level. Even experts will improve their speed of code understanding if they follow the outlined strategy.

1.4 How to Test and Train Your Skills?

We recommend you solve at least one code puzzle every day, e.g., as you drink your morning coffee. Then spend the rest of your learning time on real projects that matter to you. The puzzles guarantee that your skills will improve over time, and the real project brings you results.

To test your Python skills, do the following:

1. Track your Elo rating as you read the book and solve the code puzzles. Write your current Elo rating in the book. Start with an initial rating of 1500 if you are an intermediate, and 2000 if you are an advanced Python programmer. If you already

have an online rating on `Finxter.com`, start with that.

2. For each puzzle, if your solution is correct, add the Elo points given with the puzzle. Otherwise, subtract the points from your current Elo number.

3. Figure 1.4 shows how your Elo will change while working through the book. Two factors impact the final rating: how you select your initial rating and how good you perform (the latter being more important).

If you're an intermediate-level coder, solve the puzzles sequentially because they build upon each other. If you don't know about particular Python features, check out our five cheat sheets in the appendix Chapter 14. Alternatively, you can download all five cheat sheets as concise PDFs here:
`https://blog.finxter.com/python-cheat-sheets/`.

Advanced readers can solve the puzzles in the sequence they wish—the Elo rating will work just as well.

Use the following training plan to develop a healthy learning habit with puzzle-based learning.

1. Choose or create a daily trigger, after which you'll solve code puzzles for 10 minutes. Solve code puz-

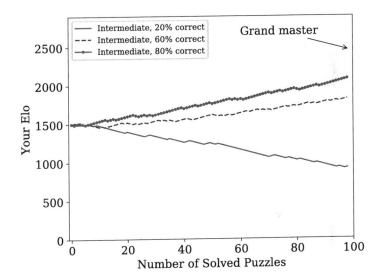

Figure 1.1: Example of how your Elo rating could change while working through the 99 puzzles. Your final Elo rating depends on the percentage of correctly solved puzzles.

zles as you brush your teeth or sit on the train to
work, university, or school.

2. Scan over the puzzle and ask yourself: what is the
   unique idea of this puzzle?

3. Dive deeply into the code. Try to understand the
   purpose of each symbol, even if it seems trivial at
   first. Avoid being shallow and lazy. Instead, solve
   each puzzle thoroughly and take your time. It may
   seem counter-intuitive at first, but to learn faster,
   you must take your time and allow yourself to dig
   deep. There is no shortcut.

4. Stay objective when evaluating your solution—we
   all tend to lie to ourselves.

5. Look up the solution and read the explanation
   with care. Do you understand every aspect of the
   code? Write questions down and look up the answers later. Or send them to us (`admin@finxter.`
   `com`). We will do everything we can to come up
   with a good explanation.

6. If your solution was 100% correct—including whites-
   paces, data types, and formatting of the output—
   you get the Elo points for this puzzle. Otherwise,
   your solution was wrong, and you must subtract

Elo points. This rule is strict because code is either right or wrong. If you miss some whitespace in the wild, you may get an error.

As you follow this simple training plan, your ability to understand source code quickly will improve. You do not have to invest much time because the training plan requires only 10–20 minutes per day. But you must be persistent with your effort. If you get off track, get right back on the next day. When you run out of code puzzles, feel free to checkout `Finxter.com`. The Finxter app has more than 500 hand-crafted code puzzles—and we regularly publish new ones.

— 2 —

Python Elo 1300-1400: *Learner* to *Experienced Learner*

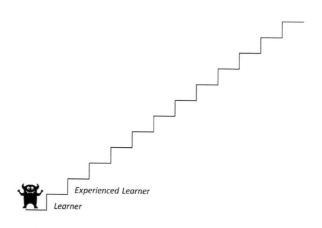

Experienced Learner

Learner

2.1 Basic For Loop

 # Elo 1348

```
n, count = 5, 0
for _ in range(n):
    n -= 1
    count += 1
print(count)
```

What's the output of this code snippet?
Correct: +10 Elo points / Wrong: -10 Elo points

First, you initialize the variables n = 5 and count = 0. The range of the for loop is from 0 to 4 (inclusive) which makes 5 iterations. Since the variable count is incremented by 1 in each iteration, the final value of the variable count is 5.

2.2   Variable Scope III

 # Elo 1367

```
def swap(a, b):
    return b, a

a, b = 1, 2
a, b = swap(a, b)
print(a - b)
```

What's the output of this code snippet?
Correct: +10 Elo points / Wrong: -10 Elo points

The function `swap()` returns a tuple of the swapped values. You assign this tuple back to the variables a and b, so global variable a takes on the value of b while global variable b takes on the value of a. Thus, the output is a - b = 2 - 1 = 1

Python Elo 1400-1500: *Experienced Learner* to *Intermediate*

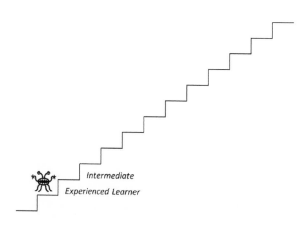

3.1 Boolean Conversion

 # Elo 1487

```
x = 0
if False or [False] or (False):
    x += 1
print(x)
```

What's the output of this code snippet?
Correct: +10 Elo points / Wrong: -10 Elo points

Any non-empty iterable has a Boolean value of True, therefore the code inside the if statement is executed which increments the value of variable x by 1. This produces the final output 1.

3.2   Tuple Constructor

 # Elo 1489

```
s = 'abc'
for _ in range(10):
    s = tuple(s)
print(len(s))
```

What's the output of this code snippet?
Correct: +10 Elo points / Wrong: -10 Elo points

First, you create string 'abc' and store it in the variable s. Second, you create a new tuple using s in the
for loop. The tuple constructor uses the characters of
the string to create the tuple ('a', 'b', 'c'). You
repeat this exact procedure nine times—without really
changing the tuple. So, the function len() returns 3.

3.3 Popping List Elements

 # Elo 1499

```
t = [1, 2, 3, 4]
x = t.pop() > t.pop() > t.pop()
t.append(x)
print(len(t))
```

What's the output of this code snippet?
Correct: +10 Elo points / Wrong: -10 Elo points

Each call of the function pop() on a list returns and removes its last element. From left to right, the first call returns 4, the second 3, and the third 2. You store the result of the comparison in the variable x and append it to list t. You initialized the list four elements, removed three, and finally appended one. So, the length of list t is 2.

Python Elo 1500-1600: *Intermediate* to *Experienced Intermediate*

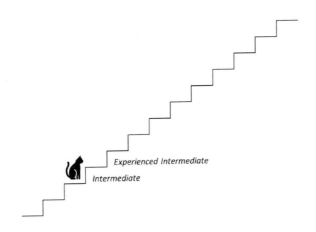

Experienced Intermediate

Intermediate

4.1 Extending Lists

 # Elo 1517

```
t = [1, 2, 3, 4]
x = (t.pop() < t.pop()), t.pop()
t.extend(x)
print(len(t))
```

What's the output of this code snippet?
Correct: +10 Elo points / Wrong: -10 Elo points

Each call of the function `pop()` returns and removes the last element from the list. From left to right, the first call returns 4, the second 3, and the third 2. Variable x holds a tuple containing the result of the comparison 4 < 3 and 2. The method `extend()` adds both tuple elements to list t. List t starts with four elements. You remove three of them. Then, you add both tuple elements. In the end, list t contains three elements, so the output is 3.

4.2   list.extend() vs. list.append()

```
# Elo 1539

t = [0, 1, 2]
t.extend([])
t.append([])
print(len(t))
```

What's the output of this code snippet?
Correct: +10 Elo points / Wrong: -10 Elo points

The trick of this puzzle is to understand the difference between the two list methods `extend()` and `append()`.

- The method `extend(iter)` takes an iterable `iter` and adds its items to the end of the list.

- The method `append(element)` adds the argument `element` to the end of the list. If you append a list to another list, you'll add one new object (the list) to the list—creating a list of lists.

You pass an empty list to the `extend()` method which doesn't change the list `t`. You then pass an empty list to the `append()` method which adds the empty list as an element at the end of `t`. Thus, the length of the list `t` is 4—three integers 0, 1, and 2, plus the empty list `[]`.

4.3　List Objects

```
# Elo 1545

t = [0, 1, [2], 3]
y = t[2]
y.append(20)
print(t[2])
```

What's the output of this code snippet?
Correct: +10 Elo points / Wrong: -10 Elo points

The list t contains integer values and another list with one element 2. The expression t[2] retrieves the inner list object and stores a reference to it in variable y. Because it's a reference, the method **append()** appends to the inner list of list t. Thus, when we retrieve the inner list again by calling t[2], it has changed and the output is [2, 20].

4.4   Python Basic Set Operations

```
# Elo 1587

a = [1, 1, 1, 2, 3, 3]
b = [0, 0, 0, 1, 3, 3]
print(set(a) >= set(b))
```

What's the output of this code snippet?
Correct: +10 Elo points / Wrong: -10 Elo points

Converting list a into a set yields the result {1, 2, 3} and for list b it yields the result {0, 1, 3}. The operator >= applied on sets checks if the set on the left side is a superset of the set on the right side. In other words: are all elements in the right set also in the left set? Since this is not the case in this puzzle, the output is False.

4.5   Length Arithmetik

```
# Elo 1587
```

```
s = '-5\\3'
print(len(s))
```

What's the output of this code snippet?
Correct: +10 Elo points / Wrong: -10 Elo points

The escape character
invalidates characters with special meaning. In this puzzle, you use the escape character to invalidate the escape character. If you print the string s to the shell, the output will be '-5
3'. For the length of a string, the escape character doesn't count. Therefore, you get the output 4.

4.6   Print Arguments

```
# Elo 1589

t = 'abc'
d = {'sep': '-', 'end': '?'}
print(*t, **d)
```

What's the output of this code snippet?
Correct: +10 Elo points / Wrong: -10 Elo points

The function `print()` takes any number of objects to be printed and also some optional arguments. You can use the optional argument `sep` to print a string between each pair of objects. The optional argument `end` can be used to modify the last character, which is printed after all the objects. By default it is the new line character (n).

In the function call `print()`, you unpack the string with the asterisk operator (∗). Therefore, each character in the string becomes a separate object to be printed. With the double-asterisk operator (∗∗), you unpack the dictionary and pass its entries as keyword arguments. The output is, therefore, a-b-c?.

4.7　Dictionary Keys

 # Elo 1598

```
x = 10
d = {x:0, 11:1}
x = 11
print(d[x])
```

What's the output of this code snippet?
Correct: +10 Elo points / Wrong: -10 Elo points

You use the value of variable x as a key when creating dictionary d. Since the value of variable x is a primitive datatype, there are no references to the same integer object, only copies—and changing the value of x will not change the key in dictionary d. So, when you retrieve the value for key 11, you get the output 1.

— 5 —

Python Elo 1600-1700: *Experienced Intermediate* to *Professional*

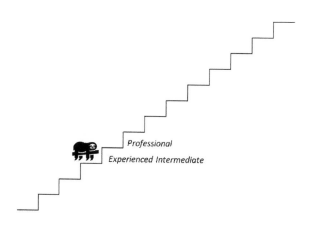

5.1 String Find

 # Elo 1602

```
s = 'bed and breakfast'
r = s.find('bed') == False
print(r)
```

What's the output of this code snippet?
Correct: +10 Elo points / Wrong: -10 Elo points

In the first line of this puzzle, you initialize variable s with the string 'bed and breakfast'. In the second line, you use the string method find() to get the index of the string 'bed' inside the string s. The string find() method returns the start index of the searched substring, or -1 if it doesn't exist. In the string 'bed and breakfast' the substring 'bed' starts at index 0, therefore the find() method returns 0.

Next, you compare 0 to False—because every integer value can be mapped to a Boolean value: 0 maps to False, any other number maps to True. Thus, comparing 0 == False results in True which is the output of this puzzle.

5.2   Slicing

```
# Elo 1639

s = 'smart'
print(s[:-100:-2])
```

What's the output of this code snippet?
Correct: +10 Elo points / Wrong: -10 Elo points

After initializing variable s with the value 'smart', you slice it. The slice starts at the beginning of the string and ends at index -100. The step size is -2, so you take every second element starting with the last element. Python ignores that there is no element with index -100 and simply takes the whole string 'smart' from which it extracts every second character starting with the last one. The final output is 'tas'.

5.3 List Arithmetic I

 # Elo 1665

```
tup = 0, 1, 2
lst = [tup]
lst.append(3)
lst.pop(0)
print(len(lst))
```

What's the output of this code snippet?
Correct: +10 Elo points / Wrong: -10 Elo points

You create a list `lst` which contains one element: the tuple `tup`. Then, you append an integer element 3 to `lst`. The method `pop(index)` removes and returns the element at position `index`. After calling the method `pop(0)` on the first list element, the list looks like this: `[3]`. As the list `lst` only contains one element, it has a length of 1.

5.4   List Arithmetic II

 # Elo 1666

```
tup = 0, 1, 2
lst = list(tup)
lst.append(3)
lst.pop(0)
print(len(lst))
```

What's the output of this code snippet?
Correct: +10 Elo points / Wrong: -10 Elo points

In this puzzle, you use the list class's constructor to instantiate a new list from tuple tup. The new list contains each tuple element as a single list element. So the list lst looks like this: [0, 1, 2]. After appending 3 to the end and removing the first element, the list still has three elements. Therefore, the output is 3.

5.5   Variable Scope II

 # Elo 1671

```
def swap():
    b, a = a, b

a, b = 1, 2
swap()
print(a - b)
```

What's the output of this code snippet?
Correct: +10 Elo points / Wrong: -10 Elo points

The official documentation states: *when you make an assignment to a variable in a scope, that variable becomes local to that scope and shadows any similarly named variable in the outer scope.*[1]

When entering the function `swap()`, Python first checks the local scope for the variable names a and b. As you assign to both variables, it considers both to be in the local scope. But on the right-hand side of the equation, you access those local variables that haven't yet been defined. Consequently, this leads to an error.

To make the code switch the values of the global variables a and b, you have to tell the function to use the global variables. You can accomplish this by adding inside the function body: `global a; global b`. Without this fix, the code throws an error.

5.6   String Find

```
# Elo 1689

s = 'apple'
print(s.find('p') + s.find('f') + s.find(''))
```

What's the output of this code snippet?
Correct: +10 Elo points / Wrong: -10 Elo points

---

[1]`https://docs.python.org/3/faq/programming.html`

The method `string.find(substring)` returns the index of `substring` in `string` or -1 if `string` doesn't contain the `substring`. In the puzzle, the first use of the function `find('p')` returns 1 which is the index of the first occurrence of 'p' in 'apple'. The second call `find('f')` returns -1 because the string 'apple' doesn't contain 'f'. Finally, for the empty character '', you get back index 0. Summing up these values, you get the output 1 - 1 + 0 = 0.

5.7   Zip Heterogeneous Lists

 # Elo 1699

```
p = ['abc']
q = ['a', 'b', 'c']
zipped = list(zip(p, q))
print(len(zipped))
```

What's the output of this code snippet?
Correct: +10 Elo points / Wrong: -10 Elo points

Python's built-in function `zip()` takes one or more iterables, say `p` and `q`, and returns a list of tuples—by pairing the i-the elements of the iterables. The first entry of the first tuple is the first item of `p`, and the second entry is the first item of `q`. The shorter one of both iterables determines the total length of the zipped result. In the puzzle, list `p` hast one element, whereas list `q` has three elements. Therefore the list `zipped` looks like this: `[('abc', 'a')]` and has a length of 1.

Python Elo 1700-1800: *Professional* to *Expert*

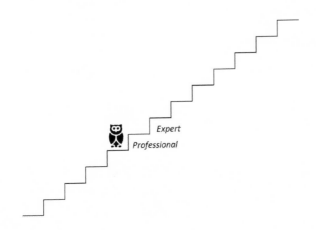

Expert

Professional

6.1   Boolean Integer Relationship

 # Elo 1721

```
num = 0
for i in range(5, 0, -1):
    num += i > num
print(num)
```

What's the output of this code snippet?
Correct: +10 Elo points / Wrong: -10 Elo points

After assigning value 0 to the variable num, you create a for-loop using the range() function. The range starts at 5 and goes down to 1 because of the negative step size. Inside the loop, you add the result of i > num to the current value of num. The result of the comparison can either be True of False. Python converts these values implicitly to 0 (False) and 1 (True). In the first three iterations the value of variable i is smaller than the values in num. Therefore, the comparison result is True and the value in num increases by 1. As soon as the value in variable num reaches 3, the result of the comparison becomes False and you add 0. The final output is, therefore, 3.

6.2   Slice Assignment Basics

 # Elo 1749

```
t = [1, 2, 3]
t[-1:] = [4]
t[-1] = [5]
print(len(t))
```

What's the output of this code snippet?
Correct: +10 Elo points / Wrong: -10 Elo points

First, you use slice assignment to overwrite the final list element with value 4. Second, you again overwrite the last list element with the list [5]. The length of the list never changes since you only exchange elements. Thus, the output is 3.

6.3   List Multiplication

```
# Elo 1755

t = [0, 1, 2]
t2 = t * 1
t[0] = 100
print(t2)
```

What's the output of this code snippet?
Correct: +10 Elo points / Wrong: -10 Elo points

The variable t points to the list [0, 1, 2] in memory. By multiplying t by 1 we create a new list, so that variable t2 points to another address in memory—a copy of list t. This is why the assignment t[0] = 100 doesn't change the list object to which t2 points. Thus, you obtain the output [0, 1, 2].

6.4 Integers in Memory

 # Elo 1766

```
x = 10
d = {'Peter': x, 'Tom': x, 'Mary': x}
x = 11
print(d['Peter'])
```

What's the output of this code snippet?
Correct: +10 Elo points / Wrong: -10 Elo points

You create a dictionary and store it in variable d. The
dictionary keys are strings, and the dictionary values
are copies of variable x. Since these values are integers,
we don't have references to variable x in the dictionary.
Thus, changing the value of variable x doesn't affect the
values in the dictionary. The output is 10.

6.5   Slice Assignment

 # Elo 1767

```
t = [1, 2, 3, 4]
t[2::-2] = [10, 30]
print(t[0])
```

What's the output of this code snippet?
Correct: +10 Elo points / Wrong: -10 Elo points

The code modifies a list with four elements using slice assignment. You replace the selected elements with t[2::-2] with the values 10 and 30. The first selected element is at starting position 2. As you have negative step size -2, you go from starting position 2 to the next position 2 - 2 = 0. In summary, you replace the element at position 2 with 10, and the element at position 0 with 30—the latter being the output of the puzzle.

6.6 Maximum With Key

```
# Elo 1771

t = [-2, 9, 0, -8]
key = lambda x: -abs(x)
print(max(t, key=key))
```

What's the output of this code snippet?
Correct: +10 Elo points / Wrong: -10 Elo points

In this puzzle, you use the optional argument key of the max() function and pass a function to it named key. The function takes one argument x and returns the negated absolute value of x. After applying the function key to list t, you get the values [-2, -9, 0, -8] as key values. Thus, the maximum is 0.

6.7 Maximum With Key

 # Elo 1777

```
t = [0, 1, 2, 3]
print(max(t, key=lambda x: x%2))
```

What's the output of this code snippet?
Correct: +10 Elo points / Wrong: -10 Elo points

The built-in function `max()` takes an optional argument `key` that expects a function. This key function computes a value for each element in the input list. The function `max()` operates on the values computed by the key function and returns the maximum depending on those values. In this puzzle, you compute the modulo 2 value for each element in the list, so that you get 1 for odd values and 0 for even values. Since 1 is the first element in the list `t` with maximum key value, the output is 1.

6.8   Variable Scoping Lists

```
# Elo 1777

t = [0]

def f():
    t.append(10)

t = [1]
f()
print(t)
```

What's the output of this code snippet?
Correct: +10 Elo points / Wrong: -10 Elo points

In this puzzle, the function f operates on the global variable t, so the call t.append(10) modifies the list stored in t. Since you reassign t to [1] and then call function f, you get the final output [1, 10].

6.9   Dictionary Comprehension

 # Elo 1787

```
a, b, c = dict((i, i*2) for i in range(3))
print(a)
```

What's the output of this code snippet?
Correct: +10 Elo points / Wrong: -10 Elo points

You can initialize a dictionary in Python with an iterable of tuples—this is called *dictionary comprehension*. The first tuple entries are the keys and the second tuple values are the values of the dictionary. You assign the three dictionary keys to the three variables a, b, and c. Since the function `range(x)` creates a range from 0 to x-1 the first key of the dictionary is 0. Thus, printing variable a leads to the output 0.

6.10 Minimum with Key

```
# Elo 1787

strings = ['flies', 'zzz', 'mammal']
first = min(strings, key=lambda x:
↪  len(set(x)))
print(first)
```

What's the output of this code snippet?
Correct: +10 Elo points / Wrong: -10 Elo points

The built-in function `min()` has an optional argument `key` to which you can pass a function. This key-function computes a value for each entry of the list `strings` and returns the minimum value based on the results of the key function. Since all elements are unique in a set, we get the following key results for the strings:

- `'flies'` -> 5

- `'zzz'` -> 1

- `'mammal'` -> 3

Therefore, you get the output `zzz`.

6.11   Slice Assignment

 # Elo 1788

```
t = [-1, -2, -3, -4]
t[t[-1]: t[-4]] = t[-1], t[-4]
print(t[0])
```

What's the output of this code snippet?
Correct: +10 Elo points / Wrong: -10 Elo points

Again, you use slice assignment to change some list elements. You select the elements at position t[-1] = -4 and t[-4] = -1 as start and stop indices of the slice. You replace the value at position -4 in the list with t[-1] = -4. This is also the first element of the list so the result is t[0] = -4.

6.12 Keyword Arguments

 # Elo 1789

```
def f(x, y, z=0):
    if z:
        return min(y)
    else:
        return max(y)

args = {'y': (2, 3, 4), 'z': 5}

print(f(x=1, **args))
```

What's the output of this code snippet?
Correct: +10 Elo points / Wrong: -10 Elo points

You pass the dictionary **args** to the function **f** using dictionary unpacking (******). Since there are keys for **y** and **z** both arguments get assigned their values as defined in the dictionary. Argument **z** has the value 5, so the if-branch is executed and, as result, you get the minimum of **y** which is 2. Thus, the output is 2.

6.13   Assignment Confusion

 # Elo 1797

```
class A:
    z = 10
    def __init__(self, x, y=1):
        self.x = x
        self.y = y

a = A(3)
z = a.z
A.z = 8
print(z)
```

What's the output of this code snippet?
Correct: +10 Elo points / Wrong: -10 Elo points

Class **A** has a class variable **z** and variable **a** is an instance of class **A**. In the instance, the value of the class variable **z** is 10—and this value is assigned to new variable **z** on the outer scope. This is a new integer variable and integers are assigned by value in Python. So, assigning a new value to the class variable **A.z** doesn't change the variable **z** in the outer scope. Thus, the output is 10.

6.14 Slice Assignment

 # Elo 1798

```
t = [0, 1, 2]
t[2:] += [t[0]]
print(t)
```

What's the output of this code snippet?
Correct: +10 Elo points / Wrong: -10 Elo points

The expression t[2:] is a slice and thus a part of t. The slice t[2:] selects only the last element of t. Because of the operator +=, you concatenate [0] with the slice— but you do it in-place without creating a new list using Python's powerful *slice assignment* feature. Each time you see a slicing operation on the left-hand side of the equation, the list may have changed. The output of the puzzle is [0, 1, 2, 0].

6.15   Unpacking Strings

 # Elo 1799

```
x, *y = '234'
print(x + min(y))
```

What's the output of this code snippet?
Correct: +10 Elo points / Wrong: -10 Elo points

First, you unpack the string '234' into two variables x
and y. Variable y is preceded by the asterisk operator *
which means that this variable receives all values which
couldn't be assigned to the left variable. In the case of
x, *y = '234' the string '2' goes to variable x and
the rest '34' goes to variable y. So, y is the list ['3',
'4'] consisting of two characters.

The minimum of ['3', '4'] is '3', but bear in mind,
the minimum refers to the lexicographical order, not to
integer values. After concatenating the strings in the
variables x and y, you get the output '23'.

Python Elo 1800-1900: *Expert* to *Authority*

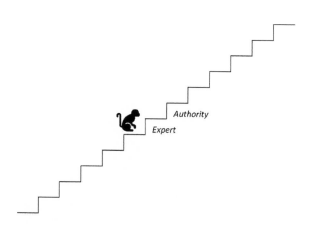

7.1 While ... Else Loop

```python
# Elo 1800

t = [1, 0, 3, 8]

while t.pop():
    if t.pop():
        break
else:
    t.pop()

print(t)
```

What's the output of this code snippet?
Correct: +10 Elo points / Wrong: -10 Elo points

For integers all values map to True, only 0 maps to
False and None also maps to False. Thus, the pop()
method as condition in the while-loop evaluates to True
as long as pop() doesn't return None or 0. The if-
statement works exactly the same. In both cases the
method pop() returns and removes the last element
from the list which is then converted to its Boolean
value. Therefore, the break in the if branch is executed and the execution of the while loop stops. Since
it leaves the while loop with break the else part of the is
not executed (the else branch of a loop executes only if
the loop terminates "naturally" without leaving early).
Thus, two elements are removed from the end of the list
and the final output is [1, 0].

7.2 Enumerating Dictionaries

 # Elo 1802

```
d = {0: 'Peter', 1: 'Tom', 2: 'Mary'}
for i, x in enumerate(d):
    if i % 2:
        print(x)
        break
```

What's the output of this code snippet?
Correct: +10 Elo points / Wrong: -10 Elo points

Python's built-in function `enumerate()` takes an iterable an returns the index and an iterable element as a tuple. It starts iterating from index 0 and the first element in the iterable.

By default, dictionaries return only the keys when you iterate over them. If you want the key-value pairs, use the method `dict.items()`. In the puzzle's for loop, you receive the indices in variable `i` and the keys in variable `x`. The first and only time that the if-condition `i % 2` evaluates to `True` is when the index is 1 since 1 evaluates to `True`. For `i = 1` we get the key 1 so the final output is 1.

7.3 Negative Slice Indices

 # Elo 1803

```
t = [1, 2, 3]
print(t[-1:-2])
```

What's the output of this code snippet?
Correct: +10 Elo points / Wrong: -10 Elo points

You use slicing starting with the last position and ending in the second last position. But as the step size is still the default value of (positive) one, the selected slice is empty. Thus, the result is the empty list [].

7.4   Iterable Unpacking

 # Elo 1807

```
x, y = '12'
y, z = '34'
print(x + y + z)
```

What's the output of this code snippet?
Correct: +10 Elo points / Wrong: -10 Elo points

Strings are iterables in Python. Therefore, you can use *iterable unpacking* to assign a string of length 2, to two variables. After the assignments our three variables x, y, z have the following values: x = '1', y = '3', z = '4'. Note that the value of variable y is overwritten in the second assignment. Since you can concatenate strings with the operator +, you get the output 134. It's a string value, not an integer!

7.5 Default Arguments in Constructor

 # Elo 1811

```
class A:
    def __init__(self, x, y=1):
        self.x = x
        self.y = y

a1, a2 = A(1), A(2)
a1.x = a2.y + 1
print(a1.x)
```

What's the output of this code snippet?
Correct: +10 Elo points / Wrong: -10 Elo points

In the constructor of class A, argument y has a default value of 1. Therefore, when you instantiate class A with only one argument in the constructor, the attribute y of the instances is set to the default value. In both instances a1 and a2 the value of y is 1 and the line a1.x = a2.y + 1 assigns 2 to instance a1's attribute x. Thus, the output is 2.

7.6 List Arithmetic III

 # Elo 1845

```
tup = [0], [1], [2]
lst = list(tup)
lst[0][0] = 10
print(tup[0])
```

What's the output of this code snippet?
Correct: +10 Elo points / Wrong: -10 Elo points

Using the list constructor, you create a new list 1st. The new list contains the same three lists as the tuple tup. However, the elements of list 1st and tuple tup neither have equal values, nor memory addresses. To put differently: The entries of list 1st and tuple tup are references to the same memory address. Therefore changing the first element in the list also changes the first element in the tuple, and the output is 10.

7.7 Default Function Arguments

```
# Elo 1849

t = [0]

def f(t=t):
    t.append(10)
    print(t)

t = [1]
f()
```

What's the output of this code snippet?
Correct: +10 Elo points / Wrong: -10 Elo points

First, you create a list t. You then define function f and pass list t as default value to argument t. Python creates the function object in memory and stores the argument default value for argument t. Default function arguments are evaluated when the function is defined (not when it is called for the first time)!

Therefore, recreating list t with a different value doesn't change argument t's default value. When you call the function f without an argument, it will use the default value of its argument t and this is still [0]. After appending 10, you get the output [0, 10].

Note: Appending 10 to the default list changes the default value of argument t. Calling function f again without an argument, would yield the result [0, 10, 10].

7.8 Class Variables and Inheritance

```
# Elo 1856

class A:
    num = 1
class B(A):
    pass
class C(B):
```

```
    pass

A.num, B.num = 2, 3
print(C.num)
```

What's the output of this code snippet?
Correct: +10 Elo points / Wrong: -10 Elo points

First, you define class A with a class variable num. Then, you create class B that inherits from class A and class C that inherits from class B. Therefore, all three classes access the same class variable num and the assignments update the same variable num. So, first you set variable num to 2 for all three classes and then you update it to 3. The output is the current value of num which is 3.

7.9   Integer and String Conversions

 # Elo 1867

```
a = str(10) + str(20) == str(10 + 20)
b = str(10) + str(20) == str(20) + str(10)
c = str(10) * 20 == 20 * str(10)
print(a + b + c)
```

What's the output of this code snippet?
Correct: +10 Elo points / Wrong: -10 Elo points

This puzzle tests your understanding of integer, Boolean, and string conversions.

- Variable a contains the result of the comparison '1020' == '30' which is False.

- Variable b contains the result of the comparison '1020' == '2010' which is also False.

- Variable c contains the result of the comparison '10' * 20 == 20 * '10' which is True.

The values get mapped to their integer values which are 0 for False and 1 for True. Summing up the results lead to the output 0 + 0 + 1 = 1.

7.10   Finding Substrings

 # Elo 1876

```
word = 'finxter'
letters = 'fix'
selected = [w for w in word if
↪  letters.find(w)]
print(len(selected))
```

What's the output of this code snippet?
Correct: +10 Elo points / Wrong: -10 Elo points

The method find() returns the index where the string argument occurs in the string on which you call the method. If the substring is not contained, it returns -1. Since you call the function find() in the if statement, the results are converted to their Boolean equivalents. Every integer maps to True, except 0 that maps to False. Therefore the list comprehension statement selects all characters from the string 'finxter' except the character 'f' because it is at index 0. Therefore, the output is the length of the list ['i', 'n', 'x', 't', 'e', 'r'] which is 6.

7.11   Integer and Float Conversions

 # Elo 1877

```
a = int(2.6) + int(-3.6) == int(2.6 + -3.6)
b = int('2') + int('3') == int('2' + '3')
c = int(-3.6) == -int(3.6)
print(a + b + c)
```

What's the output of this code snippet?
Correct: +10 Elo points / Wrong: -10 Elo points

This puzzle tests your understanding of float to integer conversion.

- Variable a contains the result of the comparison 2 - 3 == -1 which is True.

- Variable b contains the result of the comparison 2 + 3 == 23 which is False.

- Variable c contains the resuult of the comparison -3 == -1 * 3 which is True.

The values get mapped to their integer values which are 0 for False and 1 for True. Summing up the results lead to the ouput 1 + 0 + 1 = 2.

7.12 List Operations

 # Elo 1878

```
t = [1, 3, 5, 1, 3, 5]
x = t.pop(3) + t.index(5) + t.count(1)
print(x)
```

What's the output of this code snippet?
Correct: +10 Elo points / Wrong: -10 Elo points

Calling t.pop(3) returns and removes the element at index 3 from list t, which is 1.

The index of the first 5 in list t is 2.

Since we removed one element 1 from the list with pop(), the count of value 1 returns 1.

After summing up the three values, you get the output 4.

7.13 Variable Scope I

 # Elo 1879

```
def swap(a, b):
    b, a = a, b

a, b = 1, 2
swap(a, b)
print(a - b)
```

What's the output of this code snippet?
Correct: +10 Elo points / Wrong: -10 Elo points

After you assign a value to the variables a and b, you call the function swap(). Python's primitive data types like integers are passed by-value. So, if you pass a and b to the function swap(), it copies the values of the variables and creates two new local variables a and b that are only visible within the function.

The puzzle is tricky because both the global variables and the function arguments are named a and b. When calling swap(), the values of the variables a and b didn't change in the global scope—but only the function's local scope. As the global variables a = 1 and b = 2 didn't change, the result of the operation a - b is -1.

7.14 Arbitrary Arguments

 # Elo 1881

```python
def f(x, *y, z=0):
    if z:
        return min(y)
    else:
        return max(y)

print(f(1, 2, 3, 4, 5))
```

What's the output of this code snippet?
Correct: +10 Elo points / Wrong: -10 Elo points

The function f has two positional arguments (x and y) and one keyword-only argument (z). You can call function f with any amount of arguments greater or equal to 2. The first argument maps to the argument x and all the others map to argument *y. argument z is always 0 if you don't specifically assign a value to it usng z = value. In the puzzle, argument z has the value 0 and therefore the else-branch is executed. It returns the maximum of (2, 3, 4, 5). Thus, the output is 5.

7.15   Dictionary Unpacking and Assignment

 # Elo 1884

```
capitals = {'usa': 'washington',
            'uk': 'manchester',
            'italy': 'rome',
            'china': 'beijing'}
x, *y, z = {**capitals, 'uk': 'london'}
print(y)
```

What's the output of this code snippet?
Correct: +10 Elo points / Wrong: -10 Elo points

Based on the dictionary `capitals`, you create a new dictionary and update the entry for 'uk'. Then, you assign the keys of the new dictionary to the tuple x, *y, z by unpacking all values that are neither the first nor the last one in the sequence to the variable y using the unpacking operator *y (asterisk). Since there are four entries in the dictionary, variable y receives the middle values and the output is ['uk', 'italy'] because of the order of entries in the dictionary.

7.16 List Object

 # Elo 1886

```
t = [0]
s1 = s2 = t
s1 = s1 + [1]
s2 += [1]
print(t)
```

What's the output of this code snippet?
Correct: +10 Elo points / Wrong: -10 Elo points

First, you create a list with one element 0 and assign it to variable t. Second, you create two variables, s1 and s2 that reference to the same list object in memory as variable t. In other words, all three variables point to the same list in memory.

The line s1 = s1 + [1] concatenates the list [0] and the list [1] and returns the result as a new list. As a result, variable s1 points to a different list than variables t and s2.

The line s2 += [1] also concatenates two list but, surprisingly, it does not create a new list instance! Instead, it works like the extend() method: it appends the list elements on the right to the list on the left. Therefore, the variables t and s2 still point to the same memory address and printing the value of variable t results in the puzzle output [0, 1].

7.17   Recursion

```
# Elo 1887

def f(x):
    if x % 5 == 0:
        return x
    else:
        return 1 + f(x - 1)
```

```
n = f(f(9))
print(n)
```

What's the output of this code snippet?
Correct: +10 Elo points / Wrong: -10 Elo points

Function f() is a recursive function that keeps calling itself until the input value can be divided by 5 without remainder. For each recursive call, it decrements the argument value by one and adds one to the final sum. When the argument x = 5 is reached, it adds 5 to the sum, so the result is 1 + 1 + 1 + ... + 1 + 5. In other words, the function is the identity function that returns the value passed as an argument. Thus, the result is 9.

7.18   Ternary Operator

 # Elo 1889

```
translation = {'please': 'bitte', 'thank
↪   you': 'danke', 'good': 'gut'}
for word in translation:
    word = word.capitalize() if
    ↪   len(word.split()) > 1 else
    ↪   word.upper()

print(list(translation)[1])
```

What's the output of this code snippet?
Correct: +10 Elo points / Wrong: -10 Elo points

In this puzzle, many things seem to be going on, but it's much ado about nothing. The loop doesn't change anything in the dictionary d. In the last line, you convert the dictionary to a list. Since this list only contains the keys of the dictionary, the element at index is 'thank you' and, therefore, the output is thank you.

7.19 Memory Allocation

 # Elo 1899

```
x = [0]
t = [x for _ in range(3)]
t[0][0] = 100
print(t[2])
```

What's the output of this code snippet?
Correct: +10 Elo points / Wrong: -10 Elo points

First, you create a list with one element and store it
in variable x. Then, using a list comprehension, you
create another list t which contains three references to
list x. In the following line, you assign a new value to
the first element of the first list in list t. Changing the
first element of list t changes list x in memory. But list
t contains three references to the same list x. Which
ever element in list t you take, all point to the same
list. Thus, t[2] also returns [100].

7.20   Scope of Instance Attributes

```
# Elo 1899

class A:
    x = [1, 2, 3]

    def __init__(self, x=x):
        self.x = x

    def update(self):
        self.x = self.x * 2

x = ['head', 'shoulder']
a = A()
a.update()
print(A.x)
```

What's the output of this code snippet?
Correct: +10 Elo points / Wrong: -10 Elo points

The method `update()` of class A creates a new list by concatenating the list in `self.x` to itself. Because it creates a new list, the class variable x remains unchanged when calling the method. This is why you get the output [1, 2, 3] for `print(A.x)`.

— 8 —

Python Elo 1900-2000: *Authority* to *Master Candidate*

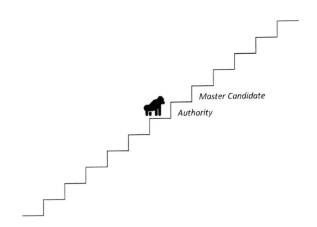

Master Candidate

Authority

8.1 Dictionary Conditional Insert

 # Elo 1900

```
d = {0: 'Peter', 1: 'Tom', 2: 'Mary'}
x = d.setdefault(2, 'John')
print(x)
```

What's the output of this code snippet?
Correct: +10 Elo points / Wrong: -10 Elo points

The method `setdefault()` returns the value of the item with the specified key. If the key does not exist, it inserts the key, with the specified value, and returns the value. Since a value for key 2 exists in the dictionary, the output is `'Mary'`—the value for the given key.

8.2 Dictionary Initialization

```
# Elo 1900

d = {bool(-1): {0},
     True    : {0, 1},
     1       : {0, 1, 2},
     (2,)    : {0, 1, 2, 3}}

print(len(d))
```

What's the output of this code snippet?
Correct: +10 Elo points / Wrong: -10 Elo points

In a dictionary, all keys are unique. If you add a dictionary entry with a key that already exists, you'll simply update the entry.

In the puzzle, you add the entry bool(-1):   0 to the dictionary. In other words, the non-zero key bool(-1) evaluates to 1 (which is the representation of the Boolean value True) and the next entry updates the first one. The third entry 1 also updates the existing one.

So, after the first three entries, the dictionary contains only one entry 1:   0, 1, 2. Only the last entry has a different key, so you create a new entry. The final dictionary has only two entries. The result of len(d) is, therefore, 2.

8.3   List Comprehension Arithmetic

```
# Elo 1901

class A:
    x = 'pandas'

t = [A() for _ in range(10)]
t[0].x = 'numpy'
t[1].x = 'sklearn'
print(t[2].x)
```

What's the output of this code snippet?
Correct: +10 Elo points / Wrong: -10 Elo points

You create a list of ten instances of class A. Since you modify the attribute x only in the first and second instances, the third instance still has its default value. Thus, the output is pandas.

8.4   Overriding

```
# Elo 1901

class A:
    def func(self):
        return self.run()

    def run(self):
        return 1

class B(A):
    def run(self):
        return 2

class C(B):
    def run(self):
        return 3

c = C()
print(c.func())
```

What's the output of this code snippet?

Correct: +10 Elo points / Wrong: -10 Elo points

First, you define class A with two methods, func() and
run(). Next, class B inherits from class A and overrides
the method run(). Class C inherits from class B and
also overrides the method run(). When you call the
method func() on instance c of class C it executes the
implementation of method run() of class C. Thus, the
output is 3.

8.5   Understanding Iterables I

 # Elo 1902

```
lst = [0, 1, 2, 3, 4]
for _ in lst:
    lst.pop()
print(lst)
```

What's the output of this code snippet?
Correct: +10 Elo points / Wrong: -10 Elo points

In this puzzle, you iterate over the list `lst` and remove the last element of the list in each iteration. To clarify what is happening, let's look at the variables' values in each iteration in Table 8.1.

Table 8.1: Variable Values After Each Iteration

Iteration	_	lst
1	0	[0, 1, 2, 3]
2	1	[0, 1, 2]
3	2	[0, 1]

As you see, the list `lst` gets shorter by one element while the iterator moves one step ahead in each iteration. Thus, there are only three iterations removing only the three right-most elements from the list. The final output is [0, 1]

8.6 Overriding 2.0

```
# Elo 1906

class A:
    def func(self):
        return self.run()

    def run(self):
```

```
        return 1

class B(A):
    def run(self):
        return 2

class C(B):
    def log(self):
        return 3

c = C()
print(c.func())
```

What's the output of this code snippet?
Correct: +10 Elo points / Wrong: -10 Elo points

In this puzzle, you have a nested inheritance hierarchy where class C inherits from class B which inherits from class A. class C doesn't override the method run() which it inherits from class B. So, when you call the method func() on the instance c of class C, the code implemented in class A is executed and runs the method run() as implemented in class B. Thus, the output is 2.

8.7 List Arithmetic (Multiplication)

```
# Elo 1908

class A:
    x = 'pandas'

t = [A()] * 10
t[0].x = 'numpy'
t[1].x = 'sklearn'
print(t[2].x)
```

What's the output of this code snippet?
Correct: +10 Elo points / Wrong: -10 Elo points

On the surface, it seems that you create a list of ten instances of class **A**. But the truth is that you only create
a list of ten references to the same instance. Roughly
speaking, your memory contains only a single instance—
with ten references to this instance. If you change the
instance variable of one instance, all list elements that
point to this exact same instance will see it. Thus,
the last change of instance variable x—setting it to the
string value `'sklearn'`—is seen by all list elements, so
this is also the output of the puzzle.

8.8   Unpacking for Pros

 # Elo 1912

```
def f(x, *y):
    t = [*x, y]
    return len(t)


x, y, z = [1, 2, 3], [4, 5], [6]
print(f(x, y, z))
```

What's the output of this code snippet?
Correct: +10 Elo points / Wrong: -10 Elo points

You call function f with three arguments—all of which are lists. There are two arguments in the signature of function f and the last one is marked with an asterisk (*). The first argument gets bound to argument x and all the other arguments get bound to argument y. Inside of function f, you create a new list t which contains the tuple y and, since you unpack the list with the asterisk operator, the elements of list x. List x has three elements, and y is one tuple. This results in a total length of four. Thus, the output is 4.

8.9 Customizing the Minimum

```
# Elo 1914

key = lambda x: -max(x)
t = (-1, -3), (-4, 9, -2), (0,)
print(min(min(t, key=key)))
```

What's the output of this code snippet?
Correct: +10 Elo points / Wrong: -10 Elo points

Tuple t consists of three elements (-1, -3), (-4, 9, -2), and (0,). Now, you first calculate the minimum of these three elements—using your own definition of the "minimum". You create a key function that associates a new integer value to each tuple that's used to determine the minimum. The key function first calculates the maximum integer value for each tuple. Then, it inverts the algebraic sign. Thus, tuple (-1, 3) has key -3, tuple (-4, 9, -2) has key -9, and tuple (0,) has key 0. Next, you take the minimum tuple using those keys—which is the tuple (-4, 9, -2) with key -9. Finally, you calculate the minimum integer of this tuple: -4. This is the result of the puzzle.

8.10   Default Arguments

```
# Elo 1919

def f(a, t=[]):
    t.append(a)
    return t

print(f(1))
print(f(2))
```

What's the output of this code snippet?
Correct: +10 Elo points / Wrong: -10 Elo points

Argument t of function f has a default value: the empty list. Internally, Python first creates the function object and, at the same time, creates the default values in memory. If you call function f without a second argument, the default value is taken. This default value is always the same list so that each call without a second argument modifies the default value of argument t. Therefore the first call of f(1) returns [1] and the second call returns [1, 2]. Thus, the output is:
[1]
[1, 2]

8.11   Unpacking Reloaded

 # Elo 1929

```
def f(x, *y):
    t = [*x, *y]
    return len(t)

x, y, z = [1, 2, 3], [4, 5], [6]
print(f(x, y, z))
```

What's the output of this code snippet?
Correct: +10 Elo points / Wrong: -10 Elo points

Inside of function f, you unpack the list x and the tuple
y. List x has three elements and the tuple y contains
the two lists y and z from the outer scope. In total the
list t contains five elements. Thus, the output is 5.

8.12   Class Variables Reloaded

 # Elo 1933

```
class A:
    members = []

    def __init__(self, name):
        self.name = name
        self.members.append(self)

    def __repr__(self):
        return self.name

w, x, y, z = A('Mary'), A('John'), A('Lucy'),
↪    A('David')
A.members.insert(0, A.members.pop())
print(A.members[-1])
```

What's the output of this code snippet?
Correct: +10 Elo points / Wrong: -10 Elo points

This puzzle creates four instances of class A. When creating the instances, you add each member to a class variable members that's a list of all instances that have ever been created through the constructor.

Note that the operation self.members.append(self) doesn't create a new instance variable but modifies an existing list (there's no new assignment self.members = ... that overshadows the class variable A.members).

Next, you remove the last element (David) from the members with the A.members.pop() method and insert it at the beginning of the list. The new last element of the A.members variable is Lucy. Thus, the result is the string representation 'Lucy'.

8.13 Swapping Values in Instance Methods

```
# Elo 1937


class A:
    x, y = 1, 2

    def swap(self):
        self.x, self.y = self.y, self.x


a = A()
```

```
a.swap()
print(A.x, A.y)
```

What's the output of this code snippet?
Correct: +10 Elo points / Wrong: -10 Elo points

The method `swap()` swaps the values of the instance attributes x and y of the instance it is called on. It is an instance method as you can see from the keyword `self` and all assignments to `self.x` and `self.y` won't affect the class variables x and y. Therefore, the output of `print(A.x, A.y)` is 1 2.

8.14   Slicing Confusion

 # Elo 1943

```
t = [0, 1, 2]
t[2:].append(t[0])
print(t)
```

What's the output of this code snippet?
Correct: +10 Elo points / Wrong: -10 Elo points

Again, your slice t[2:] contains only the last element
of list t. But you don't perform slice assignment but
simple slicing, which creates a copy of the data. You use
the method append() on the copied sublist. Therefore,
the initial list t is not modified resulting in the output
[0, 1, 2].

8.15   Short Circuiting

 # Elo 1944

```
var = True - 3 and 10 and - 1
print(var)
```

What's the output of this code snippet?
Correct: +10 Elo points / Wrong: -10 Elo points

You can read this statement as `(True - 3) and (10) and (-1) = -2 and 10 and -1`. All non-zero elements are evaluated to Boolean value `True`.

The `and` operator on two operands `a` and `b` first checks if `a` evaluates to `True`. If this is the case, it simply returns the second operand (because the second operand determines whether the overall statement `a and b` is `True` or `False`. However, the second operand is returned without converting it to a Boolean value `True` or `False`. This optimization is called *short circuiting* and many programming languages use it.

Thus, the result of `-2 and 10 and -1` is simply the last operand `-1` because both other operands `-2` and `10` evaluate to `True`.

8.16 Dictionary Comprehension

```
# Elo 1944

translation = {'please': 'bitte',
               'thank you': 'danke',
               'good': 'gut'}
d = {k.capitalize() if len(k.split()) > 1
     else k.upper(): v for k, v
     in translation.items()}
print(list(d)[1])
```

What's the output of this code snippet?
Correct: +10 Elo points / Wrong: -10 Elo points

You use dictionary comprehension to create a new dictionary d from dictionary translation. But you modify the dictionary keys in the dictionary comprehension such that you capitalize those consisting of more than one word and convert the keys with only one word to ALL-UPPERCASE letters. The values remain unchanged. After converting dictionary d to a list, you get a list of the key values, which is: ['PLEASE', 'Thank you', 'GOOD']. The element at index 1 is 'Thank you', which is the output of this puzzle.

8.17 Dictionary Pop

 # Elo 1947

```
d = {'a':1, 'b':2, 'c':3}
x = d.pop('d', 4) or None
y = d.pop('c', None) or 4
print(x or y)
```

What's the output of this code snippet?
Correct: +10 Elo points / Wrong: -10 Elo points

When you call the method pop(k) on a dictionary, the
entry with key k is removed and the value is returned.
You can also call pop(k, default_value) which returns default_value if there is no entry with key k
in the dictionary.

Since there is no key 'd' in the dictionary, the first
call of method pop() returns the default value 4. The
or between two values returns the first value that not
evaluates to False, so variable x gets assigned the value
4.

In the second call, you use the key 'c' which exists
in dictionary d so that you get the value for the given
key which is 3. As both values are not None the first
value is assigned to variable y. The last statement 4 or
3 returns 4 because its the first "True" value and the
output is 4.

8.18   Class Variable vs Instance Attributes

```
# Elo 1951

class A:
    t = [1, 2, 3]

a1, a2 = A(), A()
```

```
a1.t += [4]
a2.t = a2.t + [4]
print(len(A.t))
```

What's the output of this code snippet?

Correct: +10 Elo points / Wrong: -10 Elo points

In this puzzle, you define class A with class variable t
of a non-primitve datatype (list). When you create new
instances of class A, their attribute t holds a reference to
the same list in memory. In the line a1.t += [4], you
extend the existing list with the elements in list [4]—
the shorthand expression += only appends the elements
on the right to the list on the left without creating a new
one. Because this concatenation doesn't create a new
list, the memory address in variable t doesn't change.
Therefore, the class variable object list t is updated. In
the line a2.t = a2.t + [4], however, you create a new
list and the reference in attribute t in the instance a2
is updated. Now, it points to a new list: [1, 2, 3,
4, 4]. And variable a2.t is now a (dynamic) instance
attribute and not a class variable anymore. Whereas
the class variable t of instance a1 still hold the old list's
reference. Thus, the length of A.t is 4.

8.19   Dictionary Unpacking

```
# Elo 1965

d1 = {'a': 1, 'b': 2}
d2 = {'b': 2, 'c': 3}

def f(a, b, c):
    return max((a, b, c))
```

```
print(f(**d1, **d2))
```

What's the output of this code snippet?
Correct: +10 Elo points / Wrong: -10 Elo points

The double asterisk operator ** is used for *dictionary unpacking*. If a function receives an unpacked dictionary in its function call, it interprets the key-value pairs as keyword arguments. For example, the operation **d1 means you pass 'a': 1, 'b': 2 to the function. Since the key 'b' appears in both dictionaries, you get an error. Though both keys 'b' have the same value, you can only pass one key-value pair per argument.

8.20   Instance and Attribute

```
# Elo 1976

class A:
    x = 1

class B(A):
    pass

cond = isinstance(B(), A) and hasattr(B, 'x')
setattr(B, 'x', 2 if cond else 3)

print(A.x, B.x)
```

What's the output of this code snippet?
Correct: +10 Elo points / Wrong: -10 Elo points

This puzzle first evaluates a condition by checking if an object of class B—created with the expression B()—is an instance of class A. As class B is a subclass of A, the result is True. The second part of the condition is hasattr(B, 'x') that checks if class B has attribute x which is also True (through its parent A). Thus, the condition is True.

Next, you associate a new class attribute x to class B, which overshadows the attribute with the same name of its parent class A. As the condition is True, the attribute value is 2. If you print the parent and child attribute, you, therefore, obtain the result 1 2.

8.21 Parallel Assignment

```
# Elo 1977

t = [0, 1, 2]
t[::2] = t[::-2] = t[:2]
print(t)
```

What's the output of this code snippet?
Correct: +10 Elo points / Wrong: -10 Elo points

The puzzle makes use of the Python feature of *parallel assignment*. Here's how you could rewrite the puzzle that helps you figure out what's executed in which order:

```
t = [0, 1, 2]
x = t[:2]
t[::2] = x
t[::-2] = x
print(t)
```

So, you first assign the slice t[:2] = [0, 1] to the helper variable x. You now use slice assignment to overwrite the first and the last value in list t with 0 and 1, respectively. But in the very next line, you overwrite those two values, replacing the last value with 0 and the first value with 1. Thus, the variable t contains the new values [1, 1, 0] which is also the result of the puzzle.

8.22   Understanding Iterables II

 # Elo 1982

```
lst = [0, 1, 2, 3, 4]
for _ in lst:
    lst.pop(0)
print(lst)
```

What's the output of this code snippet?

Correct: +10 Elo points / Wrong: -10 Elo points

The loop executes three times, removing three elements from the list. You remove elements from the head of the list by calling the method `pop()` with the argument 0. So, the output is `[3, 4]`.

8.23 Advanced Mapping

```
# Elo 1987

x = 'usa'
y = 'uk'
r = min(map(max, x, y))
print(r)
```

What's the output of this code snippet?
Correct: +10 Elo points / Wrong: -10 Elo points

To solve this puzzle correctly, you need to understand the function `map()` with multiple iterables as arguments. If there is only one iterable, the function `map()` applies the given function on each element in the iterable. If there are several iterables, you apply the function to the tuple consisting of the i-th elements of each iterable—increasing the value of i until one of the iterables runs out of elements.

In the puzzle, the result of `map(max, x, y)` contains the results of `max('u', 'u'` and `max('s', 'k'`. Since maximum and minimum are computed based on the characters alphabetical order, the minimum is computed from `'u'` and `'s'` and the result is `'s'`.

8.24 Tuple Concatenation

 # Elo 1988

```
x = ((())) + ((( ),),)
print(len(x))
```

What's the output of this code snippet?
Correct: +10 Elo points / Wrong: -10 Elo points

In Python, tuples are immutable. But with the operator
+, you can create a new tuple that contains the combined
elements of the other tuples. For example, the operation
(1, 2) + (3, 4) creates the new tuple (1, 2, 3, 4).

In the puzzle, the expression ((())) creates an empty
tuple with zero elements. More specifically, it's an empty
tuple in another empty tuple in an empty tuple. Python
simplifies it to an empty tuple without any element.

The expression (((),),) creates a tuple with one element ((),) which is again a tuple with one element ().
Yes, the empty tuple doesn't have any elements but it
can be the element of another tuple.

Therefore, after creating a new tuple from the two given
tuples, you get a new tuple containing one element.
Thus, the output is 1.

8.25   Class vs Instance Variables

```
# Elo 1990

class A:
    x, y = 1, 2

class B:
    x, y = 10, 20
```

```
    def __init__(self):
        self.y = B.y

class C(A, B):
    pass

c = C()
print(c.x + c.y)
```

What's the output of this code snippet?
Correct: +10 Elo points / Wrong: -10 Elo points

This puzzle again tests your understanding of class and instance variables. You create a class C that inherits from both classes A and B. Class variables of class A are x, y = 1, 2 and class variables of class B are x, y = 10, 20.

When creating class C, you implicitly call the constructor of parent class B that creates the first instance variable y that overshadows all inherited variables and is set to the value 20 (the value of the class variable B.y).

Now, you print the sum of c.x and c.y—the latter being 20. The former is 1 because Python doesn't find the instance variable x in c so it looks at its parent classes—starting with class A. This class contains class variable A.x that is currently 1. Thus, the result is 20+1=21.

8.26   Default Object Arguments

```
# Elo 1991

def f(a, t=[]):
    t.append(a)
    return t

mylist = f(1) + f(2)
print(mylist)
```

What's the output of this code snippet?
Correct: +10 Elo points / Wrong: -10 Elo points

Since you have a list (non-primitive type) as default value for argument t, both calls of function f return a pointer to the same list. After the second call, this list consists of two elements: [1, 2]. Only then is this list concatenated to itself—and a new list object is created. Thus the output is [1, 2, 1, 2].

8.27   Default Function Arguments and Scoping

```
# Elo 1999

t = [0]

def f(t=t):
    t.append(10)

t = [1]
f()
print(t)
```

What's the output of this code snippet?
Correct: +10 Elo points / Wrong: -10 Elo points

This puzzle shows that argument default values of functions are copied—and they are only visible in the local scope. Even though you initialized argument t with the list stored in variable t, calling function f without an argument doesn't change the list stored in variable t. Inside function f, you're operating on a different list object than outside of function f. Therefore, printing t leads to the output [1].

Python Elo 2000-2100: *Master Candidate* to *National Master*

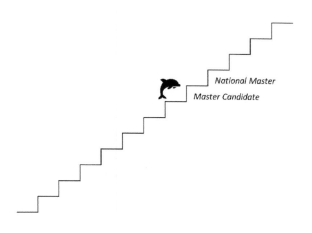

National Master

Master Candidate

9.1 String Representation

```
# Elo 2001

class Person:
    def __init__(self, name, gender, height):
        self.name = name
        self.gender = gender
        self.height = height

    def __repr__(self):
        return 'Tall '*(self.height > 165) +
        ↪   self.name


p = Person('Joe', 'Boy', 170)
q = Person('Mary', 'Girl', 160)
print([p, q])
```

What's the output of this code snippet?
Correct: +10 Elo points / Wrong: -10 Elo points

This puzzle shows the use of the `repr()` function that overwrites the string representation of a given class.

You create two persons `Joe` and `Mary`, put them into a list, and print the result to the shell. The string representation of Joe is `'Tall Joe'` while the string representation of Mary is simply `'Mary'`. Why? Because you check the condition `self.height > 165` which is `True` for Joe and `False` for Mary. A true value in Python is represented by the value 1 and a false value by value 0. Thus, if the condition does not hold, the prefix `'Tall'` is essentially skipped—which is the case for Mary.

9.2   List Operations

 # Elo 2007

```
t = [2, '32', 2, '252']
t.extend('42')
print(t.count('2'))
```

What's the output of this code snippet?
Correct: +10 Elo points / Wrong: -10 Elo points

The key to solving this puzzle correctly is the line
t.extend('42').

The method extend() adds each element from the given iterable to the list. So after you extended list t with '42', list t looks like this: [2, '32', 2, '252', '4', '2']. Finally, you print the count of the element '2'. As you can see in the list, there is exactly one string '2'. Thus, the output is 1.

9.3 Slicing Tuples

 # Elo 2010

```
t = [(1, 2), (3, 4, 5), (6,)]
x = [k[::-2] for k in t[::-2]]
print(x[1])
```

What's the output of this code snippet?
Correct: +10 Elo points / Wrong: -10 Elo points

To understand the output, let's analyze each part of the list comprehension separately. First, the context part t[::-2] yields [(6,), (1, 2)] because starting from the last element in the list, you visit every other element until you arrive at the first element of the list. The expression part k[::-2] of the list comprehension takes every second element from the tuples in [(6,), (1, 2)] starting at the last element of each tuple. The result of the list comprehension is [(6,), (2,)]. Why tuples? The reason is that you used slicing on tuples. The last element of the tuple (6,) is 6 since it's the only element in the tuple and the last element of tuple (1, 2) is 2. Now, to get the final output, you take the element at index 1 from list x which is (2,).

9.4 Zip

Elo 2055

```
d = {0: 'Peter', 1: 'Tom', 2: 'Mary'}
zipped = list(zip(d))
print(zipped[1])
```

What's the output of this code snippet?
Correct: +10 Elo points / Wrong: -10 Elo points

Using Python's built-in function `zip()` on a single iterable creates a list of tuples with one single element in each. When you use a dictionary in any function, the default value of the dictionary is its `dict_keys` iterable, in this case `dict_keys([0, 1, 2])`. Therefore the second entry in the result of `zip(d)` is the tuple `(1,)`.

9.5 Zip Iteration

Elo 2055

```python
class Person:

    def __init__(self, name, gender, height):
        self.name = name
        self.gender = gender
        self.height = height

    def __str__(self):
        return 'Tall '*(self.height > 165) +
        ↪    self.name


names = ['Joe', 'Mary', 'Tom', 'Peter']
genders = ['Boy', 'Girl', 'Boy']
height = [170, 165, 163, 160]
children = [Person(name, gender, height)
```

```
       for name, gender, height in
          zip(names, genders, height)]
print(children[-1])
```

What's the output of this code snippet?

Correct: +10 Elo points / Wrong: -10 Elo points

This is a tricky puzzle that makes use of the `zip()` function. The `zip()` function takes a number of iterables and aggregates them to a single one by combining the i-th values of each iterable into a tuple. For example, zip together lists `[1, 2, 3]` and `[4, 5, 6]` to `[(1,4), (2,5), (3,6)]`.

When zipping together the three lists `names`, `genders`, and `height`, you obtain the zipped list with three elements `[('Joe', 'Boy', 170), ('Mary', 'Girl', 165), ('Tom', 'Boy', 163)]`. Note that the list has only three zipped tuples because the `genders` list contains only three elements. Thus, the last name is `'Tom'`—which is the output of the puzzle.

9.6 Being Precise

 # Elo 2056

```
t = [0, 1, [2], 3]
y = t[2:3]
y.append(20)
print(t[2])
```

What's the output of this code snippet?
Correct: +10 Elo points / Wrong: -10 Elo points

In this puzzle, you use slicing to create a new list with one element: the inner list from list t. You assign this new list (with one list element) to a variable y. No other variable points to this new list. Therefore, appending to list y doesn't change the inner list of list t—it only produces the new list y = [[2], 20]. The inner list [2] remains unchanged. Thus, the output is [2].

9.7   Set Default Dicts

 # Elo 2061

```
class A:
    d = {True: 10}

    def __init__(self, func, *args):
        self.d.setdefault(args[0],
        ↪  func(*args))

A(max, -1, -2, -3)
A(pow, 1, 3)
print(sum(A.d.values()))
```

What's the output of this code snippet?
Correct: +10 Elo points / Wrong: -10 Elo points

The `dict.setdefault(a,b)` sets the `dict[a]` = b if the key `a` doesn't yet exist in the dictionary. Otherwise, it does nothing.

The constructor of class `A` takes a function as the first argument and a number of function inputs as subsequent values. The function inputs are stored in the variable `args` through the use of the asterisk operator `*`. Then, you take the first value in `args` as a dictionary key and the result of the function as the dictionary value and store this key-value pair in the dictionary `d`—but only if it doesn't yet exist.

You first run the function `max(-1, -2, -3)` = -1, so you associate key -1 to value -1 in the dictionary `A.d`.

You run the function `pow(1,3)` = 1 * 1 * 1 = 1, trying to associate key 1 to value 1. But the value 1 does already exist in the dictionary in the form of the Boolean key `True` that's associated to value 10 from the beginning. (Note that the Boolean `True` is represented by integer 1 in Python.) Thus, you simply do nothing in the part `A(pow, 1, 3)`.

In the print statement, you sum over all values in the dictionary `A.d` = {True: 10, -1: -1}. Thus, the result is 10 - 1 = 9.

9.8   Sequence Comparison

 # Elo 2076

```
capitals = {'uk': 'london',
            'france': 'paris',
            'germany': 'berlin'}
print(list(capitals) >
      list(capitals.values()))
```

What's the output of this code snippet?
Correct: +10 Elo points / Wrong: -10 Elo points

You can compare sequence objects to other objects with the same sequence type. The comparison uses lexicographical ordering to determine the result.

The comparison works as follows: you start by comparing the first elements of both sequences. If they are equal, the next two elements are compared, and so on, until either sequence is exhausted. If two elements to be compared are themselves sequences of the same type, the lexicographical comparison is carried out recursively. If all elements of two sequences compare equal, the sequences are considered equal. If one sequence is an initial sub-sequence of the other, the shorter sequence is the smaller (lesser) one. As soon as two item differ, the comparison stops, and the result can be determined.

In the puzzle, the first element of the first list is `'uk'`, and the first element of the second list is `'london'`. Alphabetically, the former comes after the latter, so the first list is considered larger, and the comparison returns `True`.

9.9 Definition of Instance Variables

```
# Elo 2076

class A:
```

```
count = 0

def loop(self, times):
    while self.count < times:
        self.count += 1

a = A()
a.loop(5)
print(A.count)
```

What's the output of this code snippet?

Correct: +10 Elo points / Wrong: -10 Elo points

Again, you must understand the difference between class variables and instance variables. A class variable is defined globally for the whole class. An instance variable is defined locally, and it's only seen by the local instance.

You execute the function `loop()` that modifies the instance variable `count`. If you first enter the function, this instance variable doesn't yet exist, so Python goes to the class variable and takes this one as an initial value of 0 in `while self.count < times`.

But then you execute the statement `self.count +=` 1 which is short for `self.count = self.count + 1`. This defines the local instance variable `self.count` for the first time and it sets it to 1. All future modifications are performed on the instance variable—the class variable `A.count` is still unmodified. Thus, the result is of `print(A.count)` is 0.

9.10 Name Resolution in Classes

```
# Elo 2089

class A:
    var = 1

class B(A):
    pass
```

```
class C:
    var = 3

class D(B, C):
    pass

print(D.var)
```

What's the output of this code snippet?
Correct: +10 Elo points / Wrong: -10 Elo points

This puzzle tests again your understanding of variable resolution of child classes. You print the value of D.var. Class D has no definition of variable var—but it's a child class of B and C. So Python checks first class B for a definition of variable var—without success. But class B is a child class of A which defines variable var. The value of A.var is printed to the shell which is 1.

Python Elo 2100-2200: *National Master* to *Master*

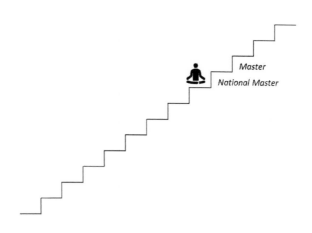

10.1 Overriding 3.0

 # Elo 2109

```python
class A:
    t = [10, 20, 30]

    def __init__(self):
        self.t = self.t.pop()

    def func(self):
        return self.run()

    def run(self):
        return self.t

class B(A):
    pass

class C(B):
    pass

b = B()
c = C()
print(c.func())
```

What's the output of this code snippet?
Correct: +10 Elo points / Wrong: -10 Elo points

This code puzzle shows the difference between instance and class variables: class variables (the ones defined without `self`) can be seen by all instances. Instance variables (the ones defined with *self*) are associated with particular instances—changing one doesn't change another instance variable.

Here's what happens in the code:

- Define the classes `A`, `B`, and `C`—the latter two are child classes of `A`.

- Initialize variables `a` and `b` with an instance of `A` via parent-child relation. Each time you create a new instance, you remove the last element of the *class variable* `t` via the statement `self.t.pop()`. Note that at this point, `self.t` refers to the class variable `t` because there's no local variable `self.t`, yet. But in the same line, you assign the result of the `pop()` statement to the *instance variable* `self.t`. Thus, instance variable `c.t` contains the value 20 that was removed in the second call of `pop()`.

- Execute the code `c.func()` and print the result to the shell. Within the function, you execute `self.run()` that returns the value `c.t=20`.

Thus, the output of this puzzle is 20.

10.2   Short Circuiting

```
# Elo 2122


t = [1, 2, 2, 1]
x = t.pop() < t.pop() < t.pop() < t.pop()
t.append(x)
print(len(t))
```

What's the output of this code snippet?
Correct: +10 Elo points / Wrong: -10 Elo points

Python's comparison operators support short-circuiting, which means the evaluation of a statement stops as soon as the final result is clear. In the puzzle, the last call of the method `pop()` is not executed because after 1 < 2 < 2 the result is already clear (`False`). So you only removed three elements from the list. After appending the result of the comparison, the list `t` contains two elements. Thus, the output is 2.

10.3   Boolean Operator Precedence

 # Elo 2141

```
print(0 not in [1] is not 0 in [1])
```

What's the output of this code snippet?
Correct: +10 Elo points / Wrong: -10 Elo points

To solve this puzzle correctly it is necessary to under-stand how Python interprets the statement `print(0 not in [1] is not 0 in [1])`. There are three op-erators in the statement:

- `not in`,

- `is not`, and

- `in`.

All have the same level in the operator precedence table. In this case, Python assumes you chain multiple oper-ations (like in `a = b = 10`) and interprets your expres-sion as follows: `(0 not in [1])` `and` `([1] is not 0)` `and` `(0 in [1])` which results in `True` `and` `True` `and` `False`. Thus the final result is `False`.

Python Elo 2200-2300: *Master* to *International Master*

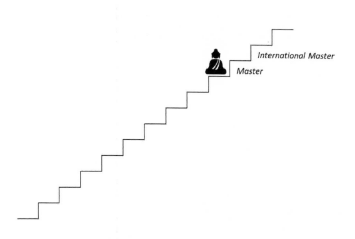

11.1 Operator Precedence

 # Elo 2209

```
a = 10 > 9.0
b = not a
print(not a == not b)
```

What's the output of this code snippet?
Correct: +10 Elo points / Wrong: -10 Elo points

This puzzle is tricky. The first two lines are easy to understand:

- First, you assign the result of the comparison 10 > 9.0 to variable a, so variable a contains the value True.

- Second, variable b gets assigned the negated value of variable a, making it False.

Now comes the tricky part. How to execute the comparison not a == not b? Is it (not a) == (not b) or not (a == (not b))? And there are more ways to put the parenthesis! The Python interpreter cannot figure it out—so, it throws an invalid syntax exception. If you solved the puzzle correctly, consider yourself a world-class Python genius! But don't worry if you couldn't solve it—this puzzle is tough, even for advanced Python coders, and it requires a deep understanding of the Python Boolean operations.

Here's how you can fix the ambiguity of the code puzzle:

```
a = 10 > 9.0
b = not a
print((not a) == (not b))
# False
```

11.2 Custom Sum

 # Elo 2288

```
class A:
    def __init__(self, x):
        self.x = x

    def __add__(self, other):
        return self.x + other.x

s = sum(A(n) for n in range(4))
print(s)
```

What's the output of this code snippet?
Correct: +10 Elo points / Wrong: -10 Elo points

This puzzle is tricky because it looks simple: you redefine the add() function on the class A to add together two instances of class A. As you've defined the add() function, you assume you can use the sum() function. However, the sum function works only on numerical values because it adds all elements in the iterable to the initial value 0. So, you get a TypeError when you try to add an instance of class A to an integer value 0.

11.3   Global and Local Variable Scopes

```
# Elo 2299

count = 0

def increment(n):
    count += n

increment(5//2 ** 2)
print(count)
```

What's the output of this code snippet?
Correct: +10 Elo points / Wrong: -10 Elo points

Since the variable `count` is of type integer (primitive type), it can't be referenced inside function `increment()`. Thus, the code throws an error. Add the line `global count` before incrementing `count` inside the function to fix the error.

Python Elo 2300-*: *International Master* to *Grandmaster*

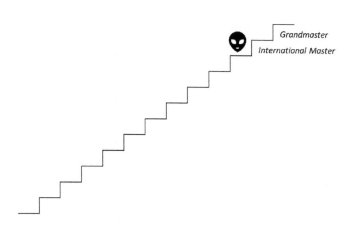

12.1 Mutability of Objects

 # Elo 2345

```
t1 = True, (), [], None
t2 = True, (), [], None
count = sum(map(lambda x, y: x is y, t1, t2))
print(count)
```

What's the output of this code snippet?
Correct: +10 Elo points / Wrong: -10 Elo points

The puzzle creates two seemingly identical tuples `t1` = (True, (), [], None) and `t1` = (True, (), [], None).

You use the map function to compare the i-th tuple elements using the *is* operator. If a pair of elements point to the same memory location, the *is* operator returns True—and False otherwise.

To solve the puzzle, you must know that immutable data types exist only once in memory—all variables initialized with a Boolean value, a tuple, or the value None share the same object in memory, if possible. There's simply no need to create multiple objects of the same tuple in memory if nobody can change the tuple value anyway. Thus, Python optimizes memory usage by sharing immutable objects among different (independent) variables.

But there's one element that's mutable: the empty list. Because of that, there are two empty lists in memory—so [] is [] returns False.

Therefore, the four elements in the map object returned by the map() function are True, True, False, and True. If you sum them up, you obtain 1 + 1 + 0 + 1 = 3. This is the result of the puzzle.

12.2 The Complement Operator

 # Elo 2499

```
y = ~(~True + ~False)
print(y)
```

What's the output of this code snippet?
Correct: +10 Elo points / Wrong: -10 Elo points

The tilde operator in Python is the complement of the bit representation of the integer. Roughly speaking, you multiply the original value x with (-1) and decrement the result by one to obtain the complement -x-1. If you start with a negative value -x, the inverse operation is to multiply it with (-1) and increment the result by one.

Thus, the expression ~True is equivalent to ~1. If you now calculate the complement, you get the result -1-1=-2. This way, the equation becomes y = ~(~True + ~False) = ~(~1 + ~0) = ~((-1 - 1) + (-0 - 1)) = ~(-3) = -(-3 + 1) = 2 which is the output of the puzzle.

— 13 —

Final Remarks

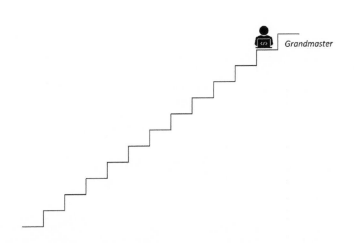

Grandmaster

Congratulations, you made it through this whole Python Mastery Workout!

By reading this book, you have now acquired a rare and precious skill: understanding difficult and tricky

Python code. You have worked through 99 advanced-level Python puzzles and enhanced your ability to think clearly. You've trained your brain to solve problems efficiently—a crucial skill for a software developer.

By now, you should have a fair estimate of your skill level compared to others—be sure to consult Table 1.1 again to get the respective rank for your Elo rating.

Where to Go From Here?

Consistent effort and persistence is the key to success. If you feel that solving code puzzles has advanced your skills, make it a daily habit to solve one Python puzzle a day (and watch the related video on the Finxter.com web app). Build this habit into your life—e.g., use your morning coffee break routine—and you will soon become one of the best programmers in your environment.

We publish a fresh code puzzle every couple of days on our website `https://finxter.com`. All puzzles are available for free. Our goal with Finxter is to make learning to code easy, individualized, and accessible.

- We worked hard to make this book as valuable for you as possible. But no book can reach perfection without feedback from early adopters and highly active readers. For any feedback, questions, or problems you may have, please send me an email at `admin@finxter.com`.

- We highly appreciate your honest book review on your preferred bookseller (e.g., Amazon). We're not spending tons of money on advertising and rely on loyal Finxters to spread the word. Would you mind leaving a review to share your learning experience with others?

- To grow your Python skills on autopilot, register for the free Python email course here: `https://blog.finxter.com/subscribe`.

- You have now stretched your Python skills beyond mastery level. Why not sell your skills on the marketplace for a few hours per week—and build your profitable side business as a freelance developer? If you want to learn how to sell your skills as a Python freelancer effectively, watch the free *"How to Build Your High-Income Skill Python"* webinar at `https://blog.finxter.com/webinar-freelancer/`.

Finally, I would like to express my deep gratitude that you have spent your time solving code puzzles and reading this book. Above everything else, I value your time. The ultimate goal of any good textbook should be to *save time*. By working through this book, you have gained insights about your coding skill level. But only if you apply your Python skills to the real world, will you experience a positive return on invested time and money. Keep investing in yourself, work on practical projects, and stay active within the Finxter community to continuously improve your Python skills.

More Python Textbooks

The Finxter textbook series helps you master computer science with a focus on Python coding. Read on to learn about the other textbooks in the series.

Coffee Break Python: 50 Workouts to Kickstart
Your Rapid Code Understanding in Python.

The first bestselling book of the "Coffee Break Python"
series offers 50 educative code puzzles, 10 tips for efficient learning, 5 Python cheat sheets, and 1 accurate
way to measure your coding skills.

Get the ebook:
https://blog.finxter.com/coffee-break-python/

Get the print book:
https://www.amazon.com/dp/B07GSTJPFD

Coffee Break Python Workbook: 127 Python Puzzles to Push You From Zero to Hero in Your Coffee Breaks

This book is the chess grandmaster way of learning Python. 127 unique and brand-new Python puzzles - each pointing to gaps in your knowledge, challenges you to guess a solution and then explains potential solutions in an easy-to-understand manner.

Get the ebook:
https://blog.finxter.com/coffee-break-python-workbook/

Get the print book:
https://www.amazon.com/dp/B07WQR91PF

Coffee Break NumPy: A Simple Road to Data Science Mastery That Fits Into Your Busy Life.

Coffee Break NumPy is a new step-by-step system to teach you how to learn Python's library for data science faster, smarter, and better. It's easy: You solve practical Python NumPy puzzles as you enjoy your morning coffee.

Get the ebook:
https://blog.finxter.com/coffee-break-numpy/

Get the print book:
https://www.amazon.com/dp/B07WHB8FWC

Coffee Break Python Slicing: 24 Workouts to Master Slicing in Python, Once and for All.

Coffee Break Python Slicing is all about growing your Python expertise—one coffee at a time. The focus lies on the crucial slicing technique to access consecutive data ranges. Understanding slicing thoroughly is vital for your success as a Python developer.

As a bonus, you will track your individual Python coding skill level throughout the book.

Get the ebook:
https://blog.finxter.com/coffee-break-python/

Get the print book:
https://www.amazon.com/dp/B07KSHLLG5/

Brain Games Python: 99 Brain Teasers for Beginners to Energize Your Brain Cells

Tired of brain fog? This groundbreaking new puzzle book revives your brain cells, boosts your computational intelligence, and launches your programming skills in Python—even if you have zero programming experience!

Get the ebook:
https://blog.finxter.com/python-brain-games/

Get the print book:
https://www.amazon.com/dp/B081NXFLZZ/

Python One-Liners:

Python programmers will improve their computer science skills with these useful one-liners.

Python One-Liners will teach you how to read and write "one-liners": concise statements of useful functionality packed into a single line of code. You'll learn how to systematically unpack and understand any line of Python code and write eloquent, powerfully compressed Python like an expert.

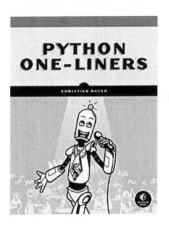

Get the print book:
https://www.amazon.com/gp/product/B07ZY7XMX8

The Smartest Way to Learn Python Regex

Google engineers are regular expression masters. They need to be because their search engine is a massive text-processing engine—when text meets computer science, regular expressions are already here.

The Smartest Way to Learn Python Regex transforms you into a regular expression master with the innovative three-step approach: (i) read a book chapter, (ii) watch the chapter video, and (iii) solve a code puzzle.

Get the ebook:
https://blog.finxter.com/
ebook-the-smartest-way-to-learn-python-regex/

Get the print book:
https://www.amazon.com/dp/B0874L1573

Python Cheat Sheets

By studying our Python cheat sheets, you'll learn 80% of Python's language features in 20% of the time. Most Python coders don't invest enough time into learning the basics, such as the core language features, data types, and language tricks.

You can download all five cheat sheets as concise PDF files. Post them to your wall until you know them by heart: `https://blog.finxter.com/python-cheat-sheets/`.

14.1 Keywords

All programming languages reserve certain words to have a special meaning. These words are called *key-*

words. With keywords, you can issue commands to the compiler or interpreter. They let you tell the computer what to do. Without keywords, the computer would not understand the seemingly random text in your code file. Note that, as keywords are reserved words, you cannot use them as variable names.

The most important Python keywords are:

```
False   True    and       or
not     break   continue  class
def     if      elif      else
for     while   in        is
None    lambda  return
```

The next cheat sheet introduces the most important keywords in Python. In each row, you'll find the keyword, a short description, and an example of its usage.

Keyword	Description	Code example
False, True	Data values from the data type Boolean	`False == (1 > 2)` `True == (2 > 1)`

and, or, not	Logical operators:
	(x and y) → both x and y must be True
	(x or y) → either x or y must be True
	(not x) → x must be false
		`x, y = True, False`
		`(x or y) == True`
		`# True`
		`(x and y) == False`
		`# True`
		`(not y) == True`
		`# True`

break	Ends loop prematurely	`while(True):`
		`    break # no infinite loop`
		`print("hello world")`

continue	Finishes current loop iteration	`while(True):`
		`    continue`
		`    print("43") # dead code`

class
 	
def
	Defines a new class → a real-world concept (object oriented programming)
	
	Defines a new function or class method. For latter, first parameter self points to the class object. When calling class method, first parameter is implicit.
		`class Beer:`
		
		`    def __init__(self):`
		`        self.content = 1.0`
		
		`    def drink(self):`
		`        self.content = 0.0`
		
		`# constructor creates class`
		`becks = Beer()`
		
		`# empty beer bottle`
		`becks.drink()`

if, elif,	Conditional program execution: program starts	`x = int(input("your val: "))` `if x > 3: print("Big")`

else	with "if" branch, tries "elif" branches, and finishes with "else" branch (until one evaluates to True).	`elif x == 3: print("Medium")` `else: print("Small")`
for, while	```# For loop` `declaration` `for i in [0,1,2]:` ` print(i)```	```# While loop - same` `semantics` `j = 0` `while j < 3:` ` print(j)` ` j = j + 1```
in	Checks whether element is in sequence	`42 in [2, 39, 42] # True`

is	Checks whether both elements point to the same object	`y = x = 3`
		`x is y # True`
		`[3] is [3] # False`

None	Empty value constant	`def f():`
		`    x = 2`
		`f() is None # True`

lambda	Function with no name (anonymous)	`(lambda x: x + 3)(3) #` `returns 6`

return	Terminates function execution and passes the execution flow to the caller. An optional value after the return keyword specifies the result.	`def incrementor(x):`
		`    return x + 1`
		`incrementor(4) # returns 5`

14.2   Basic Data Types

A house is built from bricks. Likewise, a complex data type is built from basic data types. Roughly speaking, basic data types (or *primitive data types*) provide the primitives on which the higher-level concepts are built. We introduce basic data types in the next cheat sheet and complex data types in Section 14.3.

Specifically, the next cheat sheet explains the three most important (classes of) basic data types in Python. First, the *boolean* data type encodes truth values. For example, the expression $42 > 3$ evaluates to `True` and $1 \in \{2, 4, 6\}$ evaluates to `False`. Second, the numerical types *integer*, *float*, and *complex numbers* encode integer values, floating point values and complex values respectively. For example, 41 is an integer value, 41.99 is a float value, and $41.999 + 0.1 * i$ is a complex value (the first part being the real number and the second the imaginary number). Third, the *string* data type encodes textual data. An example of a string value is the Shakespeare quote `'Give every man thy ear, but few thy voice'`.

Data Type + Description	Example

Boolean
The Boolean data type is a truth value, either True or False.
 	
These are important Boolean operators ordered by priority (from highest to lowest):
not x →
"if x is False, then x, else y"
 	
x and y →
"if x is False, then x, else y"
 	
x or y →
"if x is False, then y, else x"
	``python
	x, y = True, False
	print(x and not y) # True
	print(not x and y or x) # True
	
	## All of those evaluate to False
	if (None or 0 or 0.0 or '' or []
	    or {} or set()):
	    print("Dead code")
	
	## All of those evaluate to True
	if (1 < 2 and 3 > 2 and 2 >=2
	    and 1 == 1 and 1 != 0):
	    print("True")
	``

Integer
An integer is a positive or negative number without floating point (e.g. 3).
 	
Float
A float is a positive or negative number with floating point precision (e.g. 3.14159265359).
 	
The '//' operator performs integer division. The result is an integer value that is rounded towards the smaller integer number (e.g. 3 // 2 == 1).
	``python
	## Arithmetic Operations
	x, y = 3, 2
	print(x + y) # = 5
	print(x - y) # = 1
	print(x * y) # = 6
	print(x / y) # = 1.5
	print(x // y) # = 1
	print(x % y) # = 1s
	print(-x) # = -3
	print(abs(-x)) # = 3
	print(int(3.9)) # = 3
	print(float(3)) # = 3.0
	print(x ** y) # = 9
	``

String
Python Strings are sequences of characters. They are immutable which means that you can not alter the characters without creating a new string.

The four main ways to create strings are the following.

1. Single quotes
```
'Yes'
```
2. Double quotes
```
"Yes"
```
3. Triple quotes (multi-line)
```
"""Yes
We Can"""
```
4. String method
```
str(5) == '5' # True
```
5. Concatenation
```
"Ma" + "hatma" #
'Mahatma'
```

These are whitespace characters in strings.
- Newline   \n
- Space   \s
- Tab   \t

```
## Indexing & Slicing
s = "The youngest pope was 11 years
old"
print(s[0])       # 'T'
print(s[1:3])     # 'he'
print(s[-3:-1])   # 'ol'
print(s[-3:])     # 'old'
x = s.split() # string array
print(x[-3] + " " + x[-1] + " " +
x[2] + "s") # '11 old popes'

## Key String Methods
y = "  This is lazy\t\n"
print(y.strip()) # 'This is lazy'
print("DrDre".lower()) # 'drdre'
print("stop".upper()) # 'STOP'
s = "smartphone"
print(s.startswith("smart")) # True
print(s.endswith("phone")) # True
print("another".find("other")) # 2
print("cheat".replace("ch", "m"))
# 'meat'
print(','.join(["F", "B", "I"]))
# 'F,B,I'
print(len("Rumpelstiltskin")) # 15
print("ear" in "earth") # True
```

14.3 Complex Data Types

In the previous section, you learned about basic data types. These are the building blocks for *complex data types*. Think of complex data types as containers—each holds a multitude of (potentially different) data types.

Specifically, the complex data types in this cheat sheet are lists, sets, and dictionaries. A list is an ordered sequence of data values (that can be either basic or complex data types). An example for such an ordered sequence is the list of all US presidents:

```
['Washington',
'Adams',
'Jefferson', ...,
'Obama',
'Trump'].
```

In contrast, a set is an *unordered* sequence of data values:

```
{'Trump',
'Washington',
'Jefferson', ...,
'Obama'}.
```

Expressing the US presidents as a set loses all ordering information—it's not a sequence anymore. But sets do have an advantage over lists. Retrieving information about particular data values in the set is much faster. For instance, checking whether the string `'Obama'` is in the set of US presidents is blazingly fast, even for large sets. I provide the most important methods and ideas for complex data types in the following cheat sheet.

Complex Data Type + Description	Example
List A container data type that stores a sequence of elements. Unlike strings, lists are mutable: modification possible.	`l = [1, 2, 2]` `print(len(l)) # 3`
Adding elements to a list with append, insert, or list concatenation. The append operation is fastest.	`[1, 2, 2].append(4) # [1, 2, 2, 4]` `[1, 2, 4].insert(2,2) # [1, 2, 2, 4]` `[1, 2, 2] + [4] # [1, 2, 2, 4]`
Removing elements is slower (find it first).	`[1, 2, 2, 4].remove(1) # [2, 2, 4]`
Reversing the order of elements.	`[1, 2, 3].reverse() # [3, 2, 1]`
Sorting a list Slow for large lists: O(n log n), n list elements.	`[2, 4, 2].sort() # [2, 2, 4]`
Indexing Finds index of the first occurence of an element in the list. Is slow when traversing the whole list.	`[2, 2, 4].index(2)` `# index of element 4 is "0"` `[2, 2, 4].index(2,1)` `# index of el. 2 after pos 1 is "1"`
Stack Python lists can be used intuitively as stack via the two list operations append() and pop().	`stack = [3]` `stack.append(42) # [3, 42]` `stack.pop() # 42 (stack: [3])` `stack.pop() # 3 (stack: [])`
Set	`basket = {'apple', 'eggs',` `            'banana', 'orange'}`

| Unordered collection of unique elements (*at-most-once*). | ```python
same = set(['apple', 'eggs',
            'banana', 'orange'])
print(basket == same) # True
``` |
| **Dictionary** A useful data structure for storing (key, value) pairs. | ```python
calories = {'apple' : 52,
            'banana' : 89,
            'choco' : 546}
``` |
| **Reading and writing** Read and write elements by specifying the key within the brackets. Use the keys() and values() functions to access all keys and values of the dictionary. | ```python
c = calories
print(c['apple'] < c['choco']) # True
c['cappu'] = 74
print(c['banana'] < c['cappu']) # False
print('apple' in c.keys()) # True
print(52 in c.values()) # True
``` |
| **Dictionary Looping** You can access the (key, value) pairs of a dictionary with the items() method. | ```python
for k, v in calories.items():
    print(k) if v > 500 else None
# 'chocolate'
``` |
| Membership operator Check with the keyword in whether the set, list, or dictionary contains an element. Set containment is faster than list containment. | ```python
basket = {'apple', 'eggs',
          'banana', 'orange'}
print('eggs' in basket} # True
print('mushroom' in basket} # False
``` |
| List and Set Comprehension List comprehension is the concise Python way to create lists. Use brackets plus an expression, followed by a for clause. Close with | ```python
## List comprehension
[('Hi ' + x) for x in ['Alice', 'Bob',
'Pete']]
# ['Hi Alice', 'Hi Bob', 'Hi Pete']
[x * y for x in range(3) for y in
range(3) if x>y]
# [0, 0, 2]
``` |

zero or more for or if clauses. Set comprehension is similar to list comprehension.	```## Set comprehension``` ```squares = { x**2 for x in [0,2,4] if x < 4 } # {0, 4}```

14.4   Classes

Object-oriented programming (OOP) is an influential, powerful, and expressive programming paradigm. The programmer thinks in terms of classes and objects. A class is a blueprint for an object. An object contains specific data and provides the functionality specified in the class.

Say, you are programming a game to build, simulate, and grow cities. In object-oriented programming, you would represent all things (buildings, persons, or cars) as objects. For example, each building object stores data such as name, size, and price tag. Additionally, each building provides a defined functionality such as `calculate_monthly_earnings()`. This simplifies the reading and understanding of your code for other programmers. Even more important, you can now easily divide responsibilities between programmers. For example, you code the buildings, and your colleague codes the moving cars.

In short, object-oriented programming helps you to write readable code. By learning it, your ability to collaborate with others on complex problems improves. The next cheat sheet introduces the most basic concepts.

Description	Example

Classes
 	
A class encapsulates data and functionality: data as attributes, and functionality as methods. It is a blueprint for creating concrete instances in memory.

	``
	class Dog:
	    """ Blueprint of a dog """
	
	    # class variable
	    # for all instances
	    species = ["canis lupus"]
	
	    def __init__(self, n, c):
	        self.name = n
	        self.state = "sleeping"
	        self.color = c
	``

Instance
You are an instance of the class human. An instance is a concrete implementation of a class: all attributes of an instance have a fixed value. Your hair is blond, brown, or black---but never unspecified.
 	
Each instance has its own attributes independent of other instances. Yet, class variables are different. These are data values associated with the class, not the instances. Hence, all instance share the same class variable `species` in the example.
	``
	    def command(self, x):
	        if x == self.name:
	            self.bark(2)
	        elif x == "sit":
	            self.state = "sit"
	        else:
	            self.state = "wag
	                tail"
	
	    def bark(self, freq):
	        for i in range(freq):
	            print(self.name
	                + ": Woof!")
	``

Self The first argument when defining any method is always the `self` argument. This argument specifies the instance	``` bello = Dog("bello", "black") alice = Dog("alice", "white") print(bello.color) # black print(alice.color) # white ```

on which you call the method.

self gives the Python interpreter the information about the concrete instance. To *define* a method, you use self to modify the instance attributes. But to *call* an instance method, you do not need to specify self.

```
class Employee():
    pass
employee = Employee()
employee.salary = 122000
employee.firstname = "alice"
employee.lastname =
"wonderland"

print(employee.firstname +
" " + employee.lastname +
" $" + str(employee.salary))
# alice wonderland $122000
```

```
bello.bark(1) # bello: Woof!

alice.command("sit")
print("alice: " +
alice.state)
# alice: sit

bello.command("no")
print("bello: " +
bello.state)
# bello: wag tail

alice.command("alice")
# alice: Woof!
# alice: Woof!

bello.species += ["wulf"]
print(len(bello.species)
    == len(alice.species))
# True (!)
```

14.5 Functions and Tricks

Python is full of extra tricks and unique functionality. Learning these tricks makes you more efficient and productive. But more importantly, these tricks make programming easy and fun. In the next cheat sheet, I show you the most important ones.

ADVANCED FUNCTIONS

`map(func, iter)`
Executes the function on all elements of the iterable. Example:
`list(map(lambda x: x[0], ['red', 'green', 'blue']))`
`# Result: ['r', 'g', 'b']`

`map(func, i1, ..., ik)`
Executes the function on all k elements of the k iterables. Example:
`list(map(lambda x, y: str(x) + ' ' + y + 's' , [0, 2, 2],`
`['apple', 'orange', 'banana']))`
`# Result: ['0 apples', '2 oranges', '2 bananas']`

`string.join(iter)`
Concatenates iterable elements separated by `string`. Example:
`' marries '.join(list(['Alice', 'Bob']))`
`# Result: 'Alice marries Bob'`

`filter(func, iterable)`
Filters out elements in iterable for which function returns False (or 0). Example:
`list(filter(lambda x: True if x>17 else False, [1, 15, 17,`
`18]))  # Result: [18]`

`string.strip()`
Removes leading and trailing whitespaces of string. Example:
`print(" \n   \t  42  \t ".strip())  # Result: 42`

`sorted(iter)`
Sorts iterable in ascending order. Example:
`sorted([8, 3, 2, 42, 5])  # Result: [2, 3, 5, 8, 42]`

`sorted(iter, key=key)`
Sorts according to the key function in ascending order. Example:
`sorted([8, 3, 2, 42, 5], key=lambda x: 0 if x==42 else x)`
`# [42, 2, 3, 5, 8]`

`help(func)` Returns documentation of func. Example:

```
help(str.upper()) # Result: '... to uppercase.'
```

```
zip(i1, i2, ...)
```
Groups the i-th elements of iterators i1, i2, … together. Example:
```
list(zip(['Alice', 'Anna'], ['Bob', 'Jon', 'Frank']))
# Result: [('Alice', 'Bob'), ('Anna', 'Jon')]
```

Unzip
Equal to: 1) unpack the zipped list, 2) zip the result. Example:
```
list(zip(*[('Alice', 'Bob'), ('Anna', 'Jon')]
# Result: [('Alice', 'Anna'), ('Bob', 'Jon')]
```

```
enumerate(iter)
```
Assigns a counter value to each element of the iterable. Example:
```
list(enumerate(['Alice', 'Bob', 'Jon']))
# Result: [(0, 'Alice'), (1, 'Bob'), (2, 'Jon')]
```

TRICKS

python -m http.server <P>
Want to share files between your PC and your phone? Run this command in your PC's shell. <P> is any port number between 0–65535. Type < IP address of PC>:<P> in the phone's browser. Now, you can browse the files in the PC's directory.

Read comic
```
import antigravity
```
Opens the comic series xkcd in your web browser

Zen of Python
```
import this
'...Beautiful is better than ugly. Explicit is ...'
```

Swapping variables
This is a breeze in Python. No offense, Java! Example:
```
a, b = 'Jane', 'Alice'
a, b = b, a
# Result: a = 'Alice', b = 'Jane'
```

Unpacking arguments
Use a sequence as function arguments via asterisk operator *. Use a dictionary
(key, value) via double asterisk operator **. Example:
```
def f(x, y, z):
    return x + y * z
f(*[1, 3, 4]) # 13
f(**{'z' : 4, 'x' : 1, 'y' : 3}) # 13
```

Extended Unpacking
Use unpacking for multiple assignment feature in Python. Example:
```
a, *b = [1, 2, 3, 4, 5]
# Result: a = 1, b = [2, 3, 4, 5]
```

Merge two dictionaries
Use unpacking to merge two dictionaries into a single one. Example:
```
x={'Alice' : 18}
y={'Bob' : 27, 'Ann' : 22}
z = {**x,**y}
# Result: z = {'Alice': 18, 'Bob': 27, 'Ann': 22}
```

Download cheat sheet PDFs for free at `https://blog.`
`finxter.com/python-cheat-sheets/`.

Made in the USA
Coppell, TX
25 August 2021

61185077R00116